D0635096

Interventions for children at risk of developing antisocial personality disorder

David Utting, Helen Monteiro and Deborah Ghate

Report to the Department of Health
and Prime Minister's Strategy Unit

POLICY ● RESEARCH BUREAU ● MARCH 2007

This review of interventions for children at risk of antisocial personality disorder was commissioned by the Department of Health and the Prime Minister's Strategy Unit in 2006.

We are grateful to the Department of Health for agreeing to fund the publication of the report
© Policy Research Bureau 2007
ISBN 978-0-9555313-0-9

To obtain further copies, contact:
The Administrator, Policy Research Bureau,
2a Tabernacle Street, London EC2A 4LU
t +44 (0) 207 256 6300.
e admin@prb.org.uk.

DESIGN DeMo studio@de-mo.org.uk
PRINT   Kingfisher Print, Totnes, Devon

Contents

Executive summary

Background

A strong relationship exists between the presence of conduct disorder in children and the later development of antisocial behaviour. A wide-ranging but consistent set of risk factors is implicated in the underlying causes of problem behaviour in childhood, as are a set of protective factors that can moderate the effects on children of exposure to multiple risks. Knowledge of risk and protective factors can be used to identify neighbourhoods where universal support services are especially likely to prove effective. It can, likewise, help identify children exposed to multiple risk factors for whom targeted interventions (to prevent problems from escalating or recurring) may be effective. Although they may be more intensive and their unit costs proportionately high, such services can still be cost-effective given the high social expense associated with the development of antisocial personality disorder (ASPD). An understanding of 'what works' in addressing risk factors and promoting protective factors, drawing on examples of practice from successful interventions can, therefore, guide policy and practice development in the UK.

Aims of the review

This selective review examines the available evidence for interventions with children and young people with conduct problems and their families, with specific reference to two parenting programmes, *The Incredible Years* and *Triple P*, to the *Nurse-Family Partnership* home visiting programme, and to three programmes for families and carers of high-need children and adolescents: *Multi-systemic Therapy* (MST), *Multidimensional Treatment Foster Care* (MTFC) and *Functional Family Therapy* (FFT). Concentrating on robust evidence drawn from published reviews, evidence from Randomised Controlled Trials (RCTs) and quasi-experimental designs the review considers:

* what is known about effectiveness
* the strength of the evidence
* the characteristics of children, young people and families with whom interventions have demonstrated effectiveness
* the settings – in relation to health and social care provision, as well as geographical location and social and cultural factors – where interventions have achieved positive outcomes (or otherwise).

Summary of main findings

All of the six programmes reviewed have showed considerable effectiveness in achieving positive outcomes with children and their families in both the short and medium term (6-months to two years) at which follow-ups were conducted; in addition, the *Nurse-Family Partnership* programme showed reductions in adolescent offending and anti-social behaviour at 15-year follow-up and MST demonstrated positive results in reducing adult offending in a 13-year follow-up study where it was compared with individual therapy.

Though the specific aspects of effectiveness vary between programmes, key findings for the interventions demonstrate that they work in:
* reducing behaviour problems in children and adolescents, including diagnosable conduct disorders
* reducing antisocial behaviour, including substance misuse and association with antisocial peers
* reducing re-offending and reconviction rates for young offenders, and lowering the amount of time later spent in custodial institutions.

Where this has been trialled and evaluated, programmes demonstrate evidence of benefits and acceptability across different cultural and ethnic groups. Some also show evidence of cost-effectiveness, in that savings to the public purse outweigh the costs of treatment substantially when later poor outcomes are averted or moderated. Some also show cost-effectiveness when compared to other treatment methods. Programmes also yield evidence of benefits for parents such as improved mental health and reduced parenting problems; some also show positive results for siblings of the 'treated' child.

Key features of effective programmes

The selected programmes share a number of general principles of effective implementation (and of effectiveness *per se*). These include:
* a strong, coherent and clearly articulated theoretical basis

* professional, qualified and trained staff to deliver the intervention
* high 'programme fidelity' (core elements of the programme are consistently delivered to all users) assisted by manuals and training programmes (usually overseen and certified by the programme originators)
* flexibility within the programme to assess and meet the needs of core clientele (achieved without loss of core fidelity)
* a high degree of face-to-face work with parents and/or children
* partnership with families as a core principle
* programme delivery in community rather than clinical settings
* multi-modal/multi-dimensional approaches to accommodate different preferences and learning styles, and to tackle multiple risks and problems simultaneously
* a tiered approach so that support can be 'ratcheted up' to the next level if initial intervention is not having the desired effect
* a relatively sustained treatment period.

Issues for further consideration

Much of the evaluative work on effective interventions, with the exception of *The Incredible Years*, has been conducted in the country of origin by the programme developers. Although results are promising and based on rigorous research, it would be prudent to evaluate the rest of the programmes in the UK to consider their effectiveness in a different context. It would also be opportune to build-in a longer period of evaluation, to test the sustainability of any effects, and to ensure that better data is collected on groups for whom the interventions may prove ineffective.

Although most of the interventions described are relatively intensive and expensive, more work is needed to determine how they can best be targeted to achieve positive and cost-effective outcomes. Targeting issues remain complicated, not least in relation to the need to avoid counterproductive labelling and stigmatisation of young children 'at risk'. However, the benefits to individuals and society of preventing antisocial personality disorder support the case for a continued investment in developing sensitive and discerning risk assessment tools.

1 Introduction

Background

This selective review considers what is known about the effectiveness of interventions for children whose conduct disorders place them at risk of developing persistent and intractable patterns of problem behaviour in later life. It was originally commissioned to inform policy discussions preceding publication of the British Government's Action Plan on Social Exclusion (Social Exclusion Task Force, 2006). This lays emphasis on preventing 'deep exclusion' among a small minority of children who run much higher risks than others of experiencing a range of chronic social problems in adult life, including poor physical and mental health and criminal behaviour, alongside economic poverty. The plan also highlights proposals to pilot and evaluate a number of preventive services in the fields of parenting education, home visiting, treatment foster care and family therapy that international research shows to be highly promising ways of reducing children's exposure to risk. Evidence concerning the key features, design, implementation and effectiveness of these services provides the main focus for this review.

Antisocial behaviour can be measured in different ways, and in psychiatry and clinical psychology, severe, sustained problems in adults may be diagnosed as antisocial personality disorder (ASPD). These formal diagnoses are normally reached through psychiatric interviews with individuals as well as diagnostic schedules (Farrington, 2003). However, the most widely-used diagnostic checklist – the Diagnostic and Statistical Manual of Mental Disorders (DSM-IV) of the American Psychiatric Association (1994) specifies a *'pervasive pattern of disregard for and violation of rights of others from 15 years.'* This must be indicated by at least three of the following:

★ failure to conform to lawful social norms (indicated by repetitive criminal activity)

* deceitfulness (repeated lying, using aliases, conning others)
* impulsivity or failure to plan ahead
* irritability and aggressiveness (repeated physical fights or assaults)
* reckless disregard for the safety of self or others
* consistent irresponsibility (repeated failure to sustain employment, pay debts etc.)
* lack of remorse (indifferent to or rationalizing the mistreatment of others or stealing)[1].

From this, it is immediately apparent how closely the criteria for ASPD overlap with the definition – by law – of criminal behaviour and of a relatively small group of chronic, serious and violent offenders whose activities are not only costly to society, but also account for a disproportionate volume of total crime. For example, researchers at Cambridge, who followed the progress of 400 boys born in South London in 1953 found that 6% were responsible for half the criminal convictions recorded up to the age of 32 (Farrington & West, 1993). These chronic offenders were especially likely fall within a 12-point measure of antisocial personality that included a conviction in the past five years, involvement in fights, drug taking, heavy drinking, poor personal relationships, impulsiveness and frequent unemployment (Farrington, 1991).

For an adult to be diagnosed with ASPD there must, by definition using DSM-IV, have been a previous history of conduct disorder during childhood and adolescence. 'Conduct disorder' is itself a clinical diagnosis reached on the basis of repetitive and persistent behaviour problems. These include aggression towards people and animals, deliberate destruction of property, deceitfulness or theft and serious violations of rules, including school truancy and running away from home before the age of 13 (American Psychiatric Association, 1994). The question of whether adult antisocial personality must always be preceded by conduct disorder is not entirely straightforward since there is evidence that ASPD also often follows childhood Attention Deficit-Hyperactivity Disorders (ADHD) characterised by age-inappropriate levels of over-activity, impulsivity and attention problems (Loeber et al, 2003). The boundaries of co-morbidity between two diagnoses need not, however, cloud the central preventive issue. It is evident from the whole range of psychosocial and criminological research that all types of antisocial behaviour tend to coexist and be inter-related (Farrington, 2004). For example, classic longitudinal studies in the United States, showed how conduct disordered children were much more likely than others to grow into antisocial adults.

1 In addition, diagnosed individuals must: be at least 18 years old; have a past history of conduct disorder before the age of 15; and behave antisocially in circumstances other than during a schizophrenic or manic episode.

Those who grew into antisocial personality adults had almost always been antisocial as children and adolescents. However, in the context of this review's emphasis on prevention, it also is important to note that most conduct disordered children (between 60% and 70%) did not go on to become adults with ASPD (Robins, 1966, 1978, Robins et al, 1991). British studies have also shown a relationship between multiple symptoms of conduct disorder in boys and adult antisocial personality disorder at age 18 (Zoccolillo et al, 1992).

A chart (fig 1) prepared for the Home Office by Scott and reproduced in the Green Paper *Every Child Matters* (2003) provides an estimate of the proportion of children and young people who are persistently antisocial in age groups between 5 and 17.

Fig 1: Continuity of antisocial behaviour from age 5 to 17
Source: Research conducted by Stephen Scott (2002) for the Home Office (unpublished), cited and reproduced in Every Child Matters (p.19)

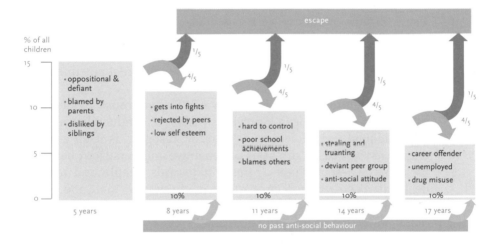

Its baseline is the estimated 15% of five-year olds who display the symptoms of 'oppositional defiant disorder' – a pattern of defiant, stubborn and hostile behaviour in the early years that includes frequent arguments, tantrums and non-compliance with parents and teachers. About a fifth can be expected to 'escape' from this high-risk group by age eight, while a tenth of those that are definably 'antisocial' at this age will not have displayed the symptoms when younger. The pattern of 'in-flows' and 'out-flows' is repeated through adolescence to a point where fewer than half the 'oppositional-defiant' five-year olds will have developed into 17-year olds with conduct-disorders.

Nevertheless, the continuities and reinforcement of childhood problems that occur among antisocial children who go on to become antisocial young adults are obvious, and indicate strong scope for preventive interventions (Sutton et al, 2004). Heavy economic and social costs incurred as a minority of antisocial children develop into antisocial adults – not least the costs of chronic, serious and violent crime – offer another compelling reason why preventive services and interventions merit careful examination by researchers and by policy makers. Five years ago, for example, it was calculated that children with conduct disorders at the age of 10 in the UK would have cost public services an average £70,000[2] by age 27. These included costs of policing, prosecution, residential care and custody as well as special education provision, social security, health and the consequences of relationship breakdown. Even then, the figure was likely to be a conservative estimate given that use of social services, primary health care, lost employment, undetected crime and victims' costs of crime were among the expenses that were not calculated. The average equivalent costs for public services used by children without behaviour problems were put at £7,400 and £24,324 for those whose early conduct problems did not develop into adolescent conduct disorders (Scott et al, 2001).

Towards prevention

Risk and protective factors

The theoretical case for viewing conduct disorder and ASPD as 'preventable' is endorsed by half a century of large-scale prospective longitudinal studies in Britain, North America, Scandinavia and New Zealand (Mrazek & Haggerty, 1994; Bynner, 1999). These have consistently identified a wide but similar range of 'risk' factors in the backgrounds of children and young people associated with an increased likelihood of later antisocial and criminal behaviour compared with other children. Some risk factors appear to be implicated – directly or indirectly – in the underlying causes of problem behaviour; others are symptoms or 'markers'. While it is clear that no single risk factor can be said to 'cause' conduct disorders or delinquency, reviews and further statistical analyses have served to narrow the field and point to those most likely to contribute to interlinked chains of causation (see, for example, Mrazek & Haggerty, 1994; Rutter et al, 1998; Anderson et al, 2001; Loeber et al, 2003; Farrington, 2004 and 2007). Risk factors have been identified that relate to individual children and young people, to their families, to their schooling and to the communities where they live. It is also clear that different combina-

2 At 1998 prices

tions of risk factors contribute to different cumulative effects and that the overall risks of conduct disorder and antisocial behaviour can increase exponentially depending on the number of risk factors to which children are exposed (Rutter, 1979). Moreover, the number of risk factors, or symptoms, appears to be a better indicator of the potential for serious conduct disorder than the pattern at any one time (Mrazek & Haggerty, 1994).

This short report does not allow space to describe in detail what the cited reviews show to be the most important risk factors for conduct disorders and criminality; but in summary they include:

Individual risk factors

Hyperactivity and impulsivity: a condition first observed in pre-school children – including those formally diagnosed with attention deficit hyperactivity disorder (ADHD). Research suggests a strong genetic / heritable component and it is consistently and robustly associated with antisocial behaviour persisting into adulthood, including chronic and violent offending (Rutter et al, 1998; Hawkins et al, 1998; Farrington, 2007).

Low intelligence: Low scores in intelligence tests completed by children as young as three have been associated with an increased risk of youth and adult offending. Intelligence as a risk factor is closely related to educational attainment (see below) but research suggests a particular connection between antisocial behaviour and inability to manipulate abstract concepts (Farrington, 2007).

Cognitive impairment: Impaired ability to foresee the consequences of actions or to understand other people's feeling are associated with subsequent offending. The tendency for aggressive children to misinterpret other children's social approaches as hostile has been linked to bullying and violent crime (Dodge et al, 1997; Rutter et al, 1998; Farrington, 2007).

Chronic ill health: Conduct disorders are more frequent among children with chronic ill health. This is especially true of children with chronic conditions affecting the central nervous system (Mrazek & Haggerty, 1994).

Attitudes condoning offending and drug misuse: Not surprisingly, young people who condone illegal drug use, criminal acts or violence are more likely to take part in them (Jessor & Jessor, 1977).

Antisocial friends and peers: While negative peer groups encourage young people to commit crime and antisocial behaviour, it is also evident that antisocial young people gravitate to negative peer groups (Patterson & Yoerger, 1997; Farrington, 2007). Antisocial young men have a tendency to form relationships with antisocial young women, reducing the likelihood they will 'grow out' of crime in early adulthood (West 1982; Pawlby et al, 1997 (a) & 1997 (b)).

Family risk factors

Low birth weight: Low birth weight and complications around the time of birth have been associated with later conduct problems where children are subsequently raised in socially disadvantaged families (McGee et al, 1984; Kolvin et al, 1990).

Poor parental supervision and discipline: Children whose parents exert harsh, cruel, highly inconsistent discipline or are cold, rejecting and neglectful are at risk for conduct disorders and early involvement in crime – itself linked to persistent adult offending (Mrazek & Haggerty, 1994; Rutter et al, 1998; Farrington, 2007). Physically abused and neglected children are at increased risk for violent crime (Malinosky-Rummell & Hansen, 1993; Widom 1989). Child sexual abuse, physical abuse and neglect also predict adult arrest for sex crimes (Widom & Ames, 1994).

Family conflict: Persistent conflict between parents, whether between intact couples or those in the process or aftermath of separation, has been associated with children's disruptive behaviour and conduct disorder (Hetherington, Cox & Cox, 1982; McCord, 1982; Mrazek & Haggerty, 1994; Farrington, 2007). An end to conflict may see children's conduct problems improve to pre-stress levels (Loeber & Stouthamer-Loeber, 1986).

Family history of antisocial behaviour: Children's conduct disorders are highly correlated with having severely antisocial parents, although the transmission mechanism may be more through poor parenting than any genetic component – unless ADHD is also a factor (Mrazek & Haggerty, 1994; Rutter et al, 1998) Having a criminal parent is, likewise, a risk factor for later offending; although this may reflect prevailing attitudes in the family, more than genetic inheritance (Anderson et al, 2001; Farrington, 2007). Parental substance abuse has been linked to conduct disorders (Loeber et al, 2003).

Parental attitudes condoning antisocial behaviour: Although closely linked to poor parenting, conflict and parental involvement in antisocial behaviour (see above), studies have linked parental attitudes that are tolerant towards crime and drug misuse to the chances of children's later involvement (Hawkins et al, 1992 and 1995).

Low income, poor housing and large family size: Growing up in a low-income family, rather than more generalised measures of socio-economic status, have been linked to later, chronic offending (West, 1982; Utting et al, 1993). The transmission mechanism to children is likely to be the additional stress that poverty places on their parents (Larzelere & Patterson, 1990; Conger et al, 1995). Inter-connected links have also been identified with poor housing and large family size (Hawkins et al, 1992; Farrington, 2007); although the underlying risk mechanisms for the latter are likely to concern other family factors (Rutter et al, 1998).

School risk factors

Low achievement beginning in primary school: Achievement and intelligence are difficult to disentangle as risk factors (see above), but children who perform poorly from junior school onwards are more likely to become involved in crime and drug abuse than others (for example, Kolvin et al, 1990; Yoshikawa, 1994; Hawkins et al, 1995).

Aggressive behaviour, including bullying: Aggression, most often in boys, is a durable characteristic of antisocial boys (Olweus, 1979; Rutter & Garmezy, 1983) that is especially visible (and measurable) at school. It has been associated with later youth offending, violence and use of illegal drugs (West, 1982; Loeber & Hay, 1996). School bullies are up to four times more likely to become chronic offenders than non-bullies. They are also more likely to father children who become bullies themselves (Olweus, 1991; Farrington, 1993).

Lack of commitment to school, including truancy: Children who feel alienated from school are at increased risk for crime and other antisocial behaviour (Hawkins et al, 1995).

School disorganisation: Attending a 'high-delinquency' school is a risk factor, although differential intake of disruptive, antisocial pupils provides the main explanation for differences in levels of student involvement in crime. But there is evidence that overall ethos and organisation of a school plays its part in protecting pupils or exposing them to risk (Anderson et al, 2001).

Community risk factors

Disadvantaged neighbourhood: Children growing up in deprived areas, characterised by poor living conditions and low employment are at increased risk for involvement in crime, including violence (Farrington, 1991; Yoshikawa, 1994). Higher rates of conduct disorder among children and young people in disadvantaged, urban neighbourhoods are likely to be mediated through the stress placed on parenting, peer relationships and other factors (Farrington 1996).

Availability of drugs: Research in the US has linked the availability of drugs and alcohol in a neighbourhood to an increased risk that young people will use them illegally and antisocially (Gorsuch & Butler, 1976). Children's access to cannabis at aged ten and cannabis and cocaine at age 14 to 16 have been linked to violent behaviour at age 18 (Maguin et al, 1995).

In a Canadian longitudinal study, the three most significant risk factors for conduct disorders were family dysfunction, parental mental disorder and low income (Offord et al, 1992). A subsequent meta-analysis of longitudinal studies concluded that the best explanatory risk factors among children aged 6 to 11 for serious or violent offending at age 15 to 25 were antisocial parents, male gender, low family income and psychological factors including impulsiveness and poor concentration (Lipsey & Derzon, 1998). Farrington, meanwhile, reported that the strongest childhood 'predictors' for his construct of persistent antisocial behaviour in adult males in the Cambridge Study were: having a convicted parent at age 10, early school leaving; hospitalisation before the age of 18; and, having an unskilled manual job at age 18 (Farrington, 1996).

Protective factors

An understanding of protective factors assists progress towards coherent preventive strategies. These, for the purposes of this report, are defined as something more than factors that would simply be the opposites of known risks (like consistent, non-violent parental discipline, or high achievement in school) They are, rather, factors that have been observed to moderate the effects on children of exposure to multiple risks (Rutter, 1990, Hawkins et al, 1992). In other words, protective factors help explain why some children growing up in what appear to be deeply disadvantageous circumstances do not behave antisocially or commit crime.

Knowledge concerning protective factors is less extensive and well-developed than the literature concerning risk (Lösel & Bender, 2003), but it is apparent that protective factors may work by preventing risk factors from occurring in a child's life, by interacting with a risk factor to attenuate its effects, or by breaking the mediating chain by which risk leads to negative behaviour (Coie et al, 1993). Some protective factors, such as those with a strong genetic component, do not immediately lend themselves to preventive action (Rutter et al, 1998; Farrington, 2000) – although it may still be important to support children who lack those protective factors in other ways. Other factors, not least the protective process described below as 'social bonding', suggest a key dimension in which conduct disorders, criminality and other forms of antisocial behaviour can be addressed:

Being female: Conduct disorder is more common in boys than girls (Mrazek & Haggerty, 1994). Boys are also more likely to show persistent symptoms of ADHD than girls. Although gender differences are less marked for 'less serious' juvenile offending, such as shoplifting, males are more likely to become chronic offenders and to commit seriously aggressive and violent acts as adults (Farrington, 1996; Rutter et al, 1998).

Resilience, self-efficacy and an outgoing temperament: Children that are temperamentally outgoing and friendly will tend to form positive social relationships at home and at school more easily than others, increasing their sense of self-esteem and self-efficacy (Werner & Smith, 1982; Rutter, 1985; Quinton & Rutter, 1988; Lösel & Bliesener, 1994). Reinforcing the protective process, a sense of self-efficacy is associated with the ability to plan ahead, forsee consequences and problem-solve (Werner & Smith, 1982; Quinton & Rutter, 1988; Bandura, 1995).

Social bonding: Stable, warm, affectionate relationships between children and one, or both parents protect children who would otherwise be at high risk of offending and drug misuse (McCord, 1982; Garmezy, 1985; Brook et al, 1990). A strong bond with a parent is also protective against antisocial behaviour when children have experienced parental conflict (Werner & Smith, 1982; Jenkins & Smith, 1990; Egelund et al, 1993). The protective concept of social bonding can be extended to association with pro-social peers, relationships with teachers and other adults providing positive role models. Children and young people with a sense of belonging and feeling valued in their families, schools and communities will be less likely to put those bonds in jeopardy through antisocial behaviour (Brewer et al, 1995; Catalano & Hawkins 1996).

Adults setting healthy standards of behaviour: Children can be positively influenced by the behaviours 'modelled' by those to whom they are attached (Brook et al, 1990; Kempf, 1993, Catalano & Hawkins, 1996).

Opportunities for involvement, social and reasoning skills and recognition and due praise: This example of several factors forming a protective 'process' is closely associated with social bonding (Radke-Yarrow & Sherman, 1990; Rutter et al, 1998). Children and young people are protected by opportunities to become more involved in their families, schools or communities (Rutter, 1996). But they also need cognitive, social and practical skills to contribute successfully and will be unlikely to persist in applying their pro-social skills without recognition and due praise (Garmezy, 1993; Brewer et al, 1995).

Life-course persistent antisocial behaviour

Another piece of jigsaw in assembling the case for interventions to prevent the most serious and persistent problem behaviour comes from research suggesting that the pathways followed by those who grow into antisocial adults and chronic, serious or violent offenders are distinctive. Using data from major longitudinal studies of children, Moffitt (1993) identified a small 'life-course persistent' (LCP) group that engage in antisocial behaviour at every stage of their lives and a larger 'adolescence-limited' (AL) group who commit crime for a relatively short period (and appear to 'borrow' or 'mimic' the anti-social behaviour of the LCP group for a while). LCP and AL offenders were also identified by Nagin, Farrington and Moffitt (1995) from the data on boys in the Cambridge longitudinal study (although the AL group had not entirely desisted from crime, heavy drinking and fighting by the age of 32).

From their experience of the Dunedin longitudinal study in New Zealand, Moffitt and her colleagues have suggested that the interplay between risk factors – relating to children's characteristics and temperament, their families and their surrounding environment – characterises the path to persistent antisocial behaviour. They suggest that the central predictive element is a process of *behavioural regulation.* This comprises social regulation by the family (such as consistent sanctions and their 'protective' use of praise) and the *self-regulation* that arises from social bonding and which the growing child begins to exercise over his own behaviour. LCP offenders, partly because of their own temperaments, do not exert the same self-regulation or experience the same external regulation as other children (Henry et al, 1996).

A somewhat differing narrative, advanced by Patterson and colleagues at the Oregon Social Learning Center, places parenting in a more central role. It is theorised that a combination of temperamentally difficult children and inexperienced parents may instigate a downward spiral where ineffective and inconsistent discipline unwittingly reinforces the child's negative, attention-seeking behaviour. Children learn to expand their repertoire of antisocial but – for them – effective behaviours at school where they are unpopular with most other children and gravitate into the reinforcing company of antisocial peers (Patterson & Yoerger, 1997; Patterson et al, 1998).

Applied prevention based on risk and protective factors

There is still much to be learned about the salience of risk and protective factors at different stages in children's development and the direct or indirect mechanisms by which they influence behaviour. Developmental sequencing also needs to be better understood, although it is evident that some factors, such as poor parenting are significant from the start of children's lives, whereas others, like association with negative peers, assume greater importance nearer adolescence (Sutton et al, 2004). Nevertheless, the effectiveness of well-designed interventions in reducing risk and levels of problem behaviour (see below) increases confidence that factors such as poor parental supervision and discipline or association with antisocial peers are implicated in the causes of conduct disorder and ASPD. Moreover, it has been suggested since the early 1990s that existing, incomplete knowledge concerning risk and protective factors can provide a legitimate basis for preventive intervention provided a 'public health' approach is adopted[3]. This argues that even when the precise, causal mechanisms are unclear it should still be possible to reduce the incidence of problem behaviour by reducing children and young people's exposure to risk factors and enhancing protective factors in their lives (Catalano & Hawkins, 1996; Farrington, 2000; France & Utting, 2005).

What kinds of prevention?

A public health approach to prevention implies, first and foremost, action taken at community level. If the aim is to reduce risk and enhance protection in children's lives, then the objective of preventing child and adolescent conduct disorders and persistent adult antisocial behaviour will only be achieved if preventive services and interventions reach enough children and young people at risk. Conventionally, such services have been (very) broadly sorted into three levels or tiers (See, for example, Hardiker et al, 1991; Utting et al, 1993):

> *Primary*: where services are designed for the whole population (or the population within a defined geographical area).
>
> *Secondary*: where services target individuals and groups

---

3 The analogy commonly used is with public health campaigns on heart disease where the general population is encouraged to reduce known risk factors such as fatty diet, smoking and lack of regular exercise.

considered 'at risk' and there is scope for preventing problems from escalating into crises.

Tertiary: where the problem has occurred and intervention aims to stop the immediate crisis and prevent the problem from recurring in future.

Increasingly, however, the key distinction drawn when describing support services is between those that are universal and offered to every family within a population or catchment area and services that are more specialist, intensive and targeted.

In the context of preventing adolescent and adult problem behaviour, universal services may have the advantage of reaching children whose difficulties and exposure to risk might not otherwise be apparent. Although outside the immediate scope of this review it is worth noting that the risk and protective factors for behaviour problems overlap extensively for other widespread difficulties, including precocious, risky sexual activity and failure to leave school with qualifications. Consequently, universal preventive services (for example, high-quality maternity care and pre-school education) have the potential to be both effective and cost-effective ways of tackling social exclusion. Universal services also hold the advantage of avoiding stigma and unacceptable labelling of children at an early age as 'potential criminals' or 'future antisocial adults' (Utting et al, 1993; Sutton et al, 2004). Assessment measures for constructing a risk and protection 'profile' of communities, hold out the further possibility that high-risk neighbourhoods can be targeted with 'bespoke' interventions (Beinart et al, 2002; Bhabra at al, 2006 (a) & (b)).

However, the evidence concerning 'life-course persistent' antisocial behaviour (also chronic, serious or violent offending) is that it is only characteristic of a small proportion of young people – and not even the majority of those who have conduct disorders as children. Not surprisingly, this gives rise to interest in whether knowledge of risk and protective factors applied to individuals can be used to better identify children for whom intensive, potentially long-term, targeted interventions may be a cost-effective option, given the disproportionate social expense associated with ASPD. Reviewers have, hitherto, concluded that risk assessment instruments are insufficiently well-developed or reliable to justify their use at individual (as opposed to community) level (for example, Le Blanc, 1998; Loeber et al, 2003). We will, however, return to this issue in our conclusions.

What kinds of intervention?

This report was commissioned to review the evidence for a number of targeted interventions that are known, from the international evidence, to have demonstrated good results in improving behaviour among children and young people with conduct disorders who are, consequently, at heightened risk for antisocial personality disorder. These are:

* Parent Management Training, including:
  * *The Incredible Years*
  * *Triple 'P'* (Positive Parenting Programme)
* The *Nurse-Family Partnership* home visiting programme
* *Multisystemic Therapy* (MST)
* Treatment (or Therapeutic) Foster Care including:
  * *Multidimensional Treatment Foster Care* (MTFC)

As will be seen, these have been rigorously evaluated in their country of origin (the United States or, in the case of *Triple P* Australia) but have also been replicated – or been actively considered for replication piloting – in the UK. We have, in addition, included a sixth intervention for detailed review:

* *Functional Family Therapy* (FFT)

This has also been identified by reviewers (for example, Kazdin, 1997) as achieving positive results in the treatment of conduct disorders and has some history of use in the UK.

We were not asked to look at other well-evidenced programmes used in the UK whose focus is more obviously on primary prevention and universal service provision. These include:

* The High/Scope Pre-school Curriculum (Schweinhart et al, 2005)
* The Strengthening Families Programme for Parents and Youth 10 to 14 (Spoth et al, 2000)
* The PATHS (Promoting Alternative Thinking Strategies) classroom curriculum for 7 to 11-year olds (Greenberg et al, 1995 & 1998)

We have, likewise, paid limited or no attention to programmes and interventions that have been strongly evaluated in the United States, but have not been transferred to the UK. These include prevention initiatives such as:

* Life Skills Training (Botvin et al, 1995)
* I Can Problem Solve (Shure & Spivack, 1982)
* Guiding Good Choices (Mason et al, 2003)

We would, nevertheless regard these as important potential avenues for overall long-term strategy for reducing persistent and severe antisocial behaviour.

What kinds of 'evidence'?

In considering 'what works?' the overview follows the approach taken by the Communities that Care initiative in its 2005 *Guide to Promising Approaches*, which is similar to that described by Moran, Ghate and van der Merwe in a 2004 report on parenting support programmes for the Home Office and the DfES. This asserts the importance of basing policy judgments about programmes on evaluations whose design and methods support the conclusion that any positive outcomes were attributable to the programme, rather than other influences or factors. In practice, this refers to evaluations conducted as randomised controlled trials (RCTs) or as 'quasi-experiments'. In the former, potential participants from similar circumstances and backgrounds are recruited before being allocated, at random, to a treatment group taking part in the programme being evaluated, or to a 'control' group of non-participants. In the latter, there is no randomised allocation, but the 'control' or 'comparison' group is made up of people who are as similar to the group of participants as possible.

One tool devised for assessing the quality of evaluations is the Scientific Methods Scale (SMS) that takes account of the methods used by researchers and whether the results, positive or negative, have been replicated (Sherman et al, 1997). This has been used to distinguish between 'what works', 'what is promising', 'what doesn't work' and – by far the largest category among parenting programmes in the UK and internationally – 'what is unknown'. Moran, Ghate and van der Merwe (2004) apply the SMS in their review of the evidence on parenting programmes, but offer an additional rating system of their own, the Global Assessment of Evaluation Quality (GAEQ) that takes account of additional dimensions, including: the quality of data collection tools; how representative the study participants were of target groups; the sample size; the appropriateness of the analytic methods used; whether variations in the content or intensity of the service were considered ('programme integrity or fidelity'), and; whether the evaluators were independent of those delivering the service.

Structure of the review

The review in Section 2 will provide a general overview of parenting programmes in an international and UK context and 'what works' in policy and practice, before giving more detailed explanation of two programmes, *The Incredible Years* and *Triple P* whose implementation is being piloted as part of the DfES 'Respect Early Intervention Pathfinder' for children aged 8-13 at risk of anti-social behaviour.

Sections 3-5 provide detailed explanations of the *Nurse-Family Part-*

nership home visiting programme which is being piloted in Britain with funding from the Department of Health, and *Multisystemic Therapy* and *Treatment Foster Care* in which there is also increasing UK interest. Section 6 describes *Functional Family Therapy* which has been applied (in a CD-Rom version known as *Parenting Wisely*) by Youth Offending Teams in England and Wales (Ghate & Ramella, 2002) and in the Republic of Ireland (O'Neill & Woodward, 2002).

Each of the detailed explanations contains information on the aims of the programme, content, implementation, staffing, training and accreditation, evidence drawn from randomised-controlled trials or quasi-experimental studies, information on types of evaluation performed, the evaluators and evaluation settings, and the outcomes produced by each programme. Finally there is a set of key points listed for each programme.

The review concludes by drawing together a series of conclusions on effectiveness and the key features of effective programmes before highlighting some policy implications and further issues to be addressed.

The table below sets out in summary the key features of the programmes overviewed, in relation to the level of intervention (primary, secondary, tertiary) and where the programme is based.

level of intervention	community setting	clinical setting	intervention duration
1 **Primary** **(universal)**	Triple P (levels 1-2)		Mostly self-directed
2 **Secondary** **(geographically** **or individually** **targeted)**	Nurse-Family partnership Triple P (levels 2-3) Incredible Years FFT	FFT	2-5 years – from prenatal to the child's second birthday Self directed plus some sessions 30 hours 8-12 hours
3 **Tertiary** **(individually** **targeted)**	Triple P (levels 4-5) FFT MST MTFC	Triple P (levels 4-5) FFT	10-18 hours approx 26-30 hours 60 hours 6-9 months in placement

2 Parenting programmes

Background

'Parenting programme' is a label applied to overlapping types of intervention that have variously (and sometime interchangeably) been described as 'parenting support', 'parenting education', 'parent skills training' and 'family support'. Definitions are sometimes broad enough to include ante-natal health services, day care nurseries, family therapy and pre-school education. In terms of delivery they may include home visiting programmes and one-to-one clinical services for individual families, as well as interventions provided in group settings. Considerable overlap also exists between the key components of parenting programmes, even when their theoretical starting points appear to be different. A broad distinction can be made between 'behavioural' programmes focused primarily on changing children's behaviour and 'cognitive' programmes where the emphasis is on changing the thinking, attitudes and beliefs of parents and improving interpersonal relationships within families (Moran et al, 2004).

Reviews such as that conducted for the DfES and Home Office by Moran and colleagues (2004) have generally found that programmes designed to improve parents' responsiveness and skills can have a positive impact on the well-being and behaviour of both parents and children. But it is also apparent that while 'behavioural' and 'cognitive' models can both benefit parents, behavioural, skills-based programmes have been more successful in achieving a measurable impact on children (for example, Barlow, 1999; Moran et al, 2004). Where children's behaviour problems are severe enough to be diagnosed as conduct disorders there is evidence that group-based parenting programmes such as *The Incredible Years* (see below) may be more cost-effective than one-to-one 'clinical' programmes (Cunningham et al, 1995).

There are also parenting programmes that include components added to tackle other family problems that may be placing parents under stress; for example more intensive levels of the *Triple P* programme described below. Training programmes in parenting skills can also benefit children with attention deficit hyperactivity disorders (ADHD). One randomised controlled trial of a parenting programme for families of pre-school children in the UK found improvements in ADHD symptoms were maintained for up to 15 weeks after treatment. This suggests the case for parenting programmes as a component in community support services for children with ADHD, alongside drug treatment and cognitive-behavioural training for children themselves (Purdie et al, 2002). It also chimes with the findings of a major trial in the United States, involving 579 children aged 7 to 9, where managed medication and a combined programme of managed medication with behavioural treatments achieved greater improvements in children's behaviour, social skills and family relations than the behavioural treatments alone or 'treatment as usual' in the community (Swanson et al, 2002).

Some key research messages concerning parenting support for policy makers, service planners and practitioners identified by Moran et al (2004) are listed below.

- Early and later interventions (although early interventions report better, more durable outcomes for children).
- Programmes with a strong underlying theory and model of how they will improve outcomes for children and parents.
- Programmes with measurable, concrete objectives.
- Universal services, supporting parents and children across whole communities.
- Targeted services, aimed at groups of families or individuals deemed at particular risk for parenting difficulties.
- Programmes that pay careful attention to 'getting', 'keeping' and 'engaging' parents.
- Services with a variety of referral routes.
- Programmes with more than one method of delivery.
- Group work, where parents can benefit from working with other parents who share their experiences.
- Individual work where problems are severe or entrenched, or parents are not ready or able to work in a group (home visiting is often a component).
- Programmes using interactive teaching methods, rather than talk-based 'instruction'.

- Programmes that are carefully structured with a supporting manual or curriculum to ensure 'programme integrity and fidelity'.
- Delivery by appropriately trained and skilled staff (backed by effective management, support and supervision).
- Programmes delivered over longer periods (e.g. three or more months), with 'booster' sessions for families with severe problems).
- Shorter, low-level services for delivering factual information and advice about child development and behaviour.
- 'Behavioural' programmes focusing on specific parenting skills and practical 'take home' tips for changing more complex parenting and influencing children's behaviour.
- 'Cognitive' programmes that aim to change beliefs, attitudes and self-perceptions about parenting.
- Programmes that work in parallel with parents, families and children (though not necessarily at the same time).

Source: Moran, Ghate & van der Merwe (2004)

Parenting programmes tend to target parents according the ages of their children. They also vary according to the severity of the problems that families are experiencing. While some are intended to be universally suitable for any parent (or grandparent), others are designed for parents of children with diagnosable conduct disorders and sometimes as a targeted component of intensive service packages for parents of 'looked after' children and other families in crisis.

In this section, as elsewhere, the focus is on evidence concerning rigorously evaluated programmes that have demonstrated effectiveness in improving behaviour among children and young people at risk of antisocial personality disorder. It will be seen that the programmes examined as case studies not only satisfy the 'what works' criteria described in Section 1, but also have well-developed training and accreditation procedures that can be used to support implementation in the UK and make it more likely that positive outcomes can be replicated.

Parent Management Training

'Parent Management Training' (PMT) is a term used to describe a group of parenting programmes that have evolved from 'behavioural' treatment programmes since the 1960s. These were built around an understanding that human behaviour in applied settings could be influenced though changes in the attention and consequences provided by others (Kazdin, 2005).

According to a recent overview by Kazdin (2005) interventions described as PMT are distinguished by four interrelated components:

* a conceptual view of how to change social, emotional and behavioural problems
* a set of principles and techniques that follow from the conceptual view
* development of specific parenting skills through practice, role play and other active training methods
* integration of assessment and evaluation in treatment and treatment decision-making.

A helpful starting point for any description of effective parenting programmes is the work of Gerald Patterson and colleagues at the Oregon Social Learning Center (OSLC). For 40 years, they have not only contributed to theoretical understanding of the part that 'coercive' parent-child relationships play in the development of conduct problems, but also devised and implemented practical parenting interventions for promoting positive, social behaviour (e.g. Patterson, 1982). Their programmes and research studies have made an important contribution to the approach and design of other positively-evaluated programmes described in this review, including *The Incredible Years* (Webster-Stratton, 2001), *Triple P* (Sanders, 1999), *Multi-dimensional Treatment Foster Care* (Chamberlain, 1998) and *Multisystemic Therapy* (Henggeler, 1997).

A pioneering feature of the Oregon studies has been the direct observation of parent-child interactions in the home, including a scoring system for 'aversive' behaviour (Bank et al, 1987). This has contributed to an understanding that teaching parents to encourage positive behaviour, negotiate with children and offer praise and rewards is necessary, but insufficient (Patterson & Narrett, 1990). Consistent and non-violent discipline to weaken aggression and provide dependable consequences for negative, non-compliant behaviour is also required. The OSLC's *Parent Management Training* (PMT) programme encourages parents to deny children the attention they are seeking for their low-level, negative behaviour. But where this is not possible, it promotes the use of now-familiar sanctions such as 'time out' where children are sent to cool off in an uninteresting room, and the award or removal of 'points' for positive behaviour linked to a system of rewards or consequences. Parents are also trained to 'pinpoint' children's behaviour, keeping track of how they treat other family members and whether they are 'minding' routinely expected tasks such as homework or household chores.

In a classic clinical study of training for the parents of 'severely out of control' children aged 3 to 12, Patterson and colleagues (1982) succeeded in bringing the behaviour of two thirds within a normal range, compared with one third in a control group who were receiving other treatments. This improvement persisted for at least a year. However, alongside its positive findings the study identified two other issues that have recurred through subsequent parenting research. One concerned targeting: a small sub-sample of children known to steal showed improved conduct, but were no less likely to be in trouble with the law at age 14 than 'stealers' in the control group. The other concerned recruitment and retention of parents: the drop-out rate in Patterson's relatively early experiments was around 25% (Graham, 1990).

Combined parenting and child-focused interventions

Subsequent trials involving PMT have sought to reinforce its effectiveness through 'combined interventions' with integrated components for children and young people. In Canada, Tremblay and colleagues (1992, 1995) devised and evaluated the *Preventive Treatment Program*, working with 250 aggressive and hyperactive boys aged 7 to 9, combining anger management and interpersonal and social skills training with a parenting programme based on PMT. By age 12, boys in the experimental group were performing better in school than those in two different control groups and were less involved in crime, fighting and heavy drinking. By age 15, differences in self and teacher-reported antisocial behaviour were even wider (although there was no significant difference in arrests or court referrals). Kazdin and colleagues (1992) meanwhile described an experiment in which children aged 7 to 13 displaying severe antisocial behaviour were randomly assigned to three different groups: one where the children were trained in problem-solving skills, one where parents took part in PMT and a third where both the children and their parents were treated. At one-year follow-up, the combined treatment group had the highest percentage of children whose behaviour had been brought within a normal range. A combined intervention for children with early-onset conduct problems using *The Incredible Years* programme (Webster-Stratton & Hammond, 1997) produced comparable results (see below).

More equivocal results emerged from a trial intervention in Massachusetts for 5-year old children screened for symptoms of behavioural and emotional problems, including ADHD. Families were allocated to:

* a 10-week parenting course followed by monthly booster sessions
* an intensive classroom social skills programme for children
* a combined intervention group
* an untreated control group.

Evaluation showed improvements in attention problems and aggression among children who participated in the classroom programme, but a lack of improvement across the experimental groups in measures of behaviour at home. This was ascribed to implementation difficulties, especially to low attendance rates at the parenting groups (Barkley et al, 2000).

In addition it is important to note the potential for unintended treatment ('iatrogenic') effects and for components in combined interventions to work in opposite directions. In Oregon, an *Adolescent Transitions Program* (ATP) programme to prevent escalating problem behaviour among 'high-risk' boys and girls was evaluated by randomly assigning 158 families of 11 to 14-year olds to four conditions:
* a parenting skills group targeting family management practices and communication skills
* a teen group where young people attended sessions on self-regulation, and social and problem-solving skills
* a group where the parenting and teen interventions were combined
* a 'self-directed change' group where parents only received intervention newsletters and videos.

Follow-up after a year found positive improvements in parent-child interaction in families assigned to either the parenting or teen-focus groups. However, immediate post-treatment improvements in antisocial behaviour rated by teachers had begun to fade and young people involved in the teen groups had worse behaviour ratings and higher tobacco us than those in the other intervention groups. This led the authors to conclude that it may be "inadvisable to aggregate high-risk youths into groups"[4] (Dishion & Andrews, 1995; Dishion et al 1999). The programme has since evolved into a 'tiered' intervention where support is made available at three different levels: 'universal'; 'selective' and 'indicated'. The latter is targeted, through use of a 'family check-up' instrument, at families assessed as in need of professional services, including behavioural family therapy and parenting groups.

In the United States, the largest-scale trial of a long-term, combined intervention to prevent chronic and severe conduct problems is the *Fast Track* programme, being implemented nationally in four different sites. Screening was used to identify nearly 900 children aged 5-6 assessed as being in the top 10% for antisocial behaviour. The

---

4 Small sample sizes did not allow the authors to report on sub-samples in their 'high risk' groups, including those with diagnosable conduct disorders.

children were randomly assigned to an experimental or control group. Designed to develop into an 11-year programme of therapeutic support services, the initiative specifically built on the findings of Tremblay and colleagues (see above). Its intensive starting point was a specially-revised version of the PATHS cognitive-behavioural curriculum (Greenberg at al., 1995 & 1998), together with other social skills training, school tutoring, home visiting and parent training. After the first year, the evaluators identified modest reductions in children's aggressive, disruptive and oppositional behaviour as well as improvements in parent-child interactions at home and more appropriate and consistent discipline (Conduct Problems Prevention Research Group, 1999). After three years, participants were less likely to show signs of serious conduct problems than children in the control group and teachers reported lower rates of aggressive, disruptive and disobedient behaviour. Parents of children in the experimental group used less physical punishment, while the children exhibited better social and problem-solving skills (Conduct Problems Prevention Research Group, 2002). Longer-term outcomes as reported on the Fast Track website are also positive (Conduct Problems Prevention Research Group, 2006). Six years plus following intervention, high-risk children aged 13-14 years from the experimental group had rather lower arrest rates compared to the control group (38% v 42%). Psychiatric interviews the following year also suggest that the intervention reduced conduct disorders by over a third – from 27 percent (the control group) to 17 percent in the experimental group.

The Incredible Years

Developed over 25 years by Prof. Carolyn Webster-Stratton and colleagues based in Seattle, *The Incredible Years* parenting programmes have been positively and rigorously evaluated in community settings in Wales and England as well as the United States. The programmes were developed to promote positive, research-proven parenting and teaching practices that strengthen children's problem-solving abilities and social competence and reduce aggression at home and in school.

Aims

* to prevent, reduce and treat aggression and conduct problems in young children;
* to enhance child social competence.
  Additional goals are:
* to promote parent competencies
* to strengthen family relationships
* to promote teaching competencies
* to enhance home-school connections.

Content

Webster-Stratton's original parent training programme has been expanded and adjusted to meet the needs of parents with children in different age groups, of primary school teachers and of children themselves. This range includes a 'BASIC' 12-14 week programme of 2.5-hour sessions that has been purpose-designed for parents of children aged 2 to 7. Groups can be of 10 to 14 parents. As with all *Incredible Years* programmes, the approach is based on 'videotape modelling' where parents discuss video clips that show parents using a range of strategies to deal with everyday situations with their child. The videotapes depict families from a diverse range of backgrounds. The BASIC programme emphasises parenting skills known to promote children's social competence and reduce behaviour problems, including effective, non-violent strategies for managing negative behaviour. The main topics include:

* how to play with your child
* how to help your child to learn
* effective praise and encouragement
* how to motivate your child
* how to follow through with limits and rules
* handling misbehaviour (including the use of 'time out')
* problem solving.

A supplementary 'ADVANCE' programme focuses on adult relationship and problem-solving skills as a response to family risk factors such as depression, marital conflict and poor anger management. This is delivered through weekly sessions lasting approximately two hours each over ten to twelve weeks (Webster-Stratton, 2001).

Further programmes include *The Incredible Years* school-age parent training series which includes three videotapes for parents of children aged 5 to 12 years old. Again this is a multi-cultural programme emphasising parental monitoring, problem-solving with children and family problem-solving techniques. There is also *The Incredible Years* teacher training programme designed to train teachers in classroom management skills including how to encourage and motivate children through the use of incentives. The *Dina-Dinosaur* child training series delivered to children two to three times a week and lasting approximately 50 minutes on each occasion teaches children conflict management and friendship skills, appropriate classroom behaviour and empathy. The skills, like the parent and teacher training programmes, are delivered via the use of videotapes and also include the use of life-size puppets (Webster-Stratton, 2001).

Implementation

Trained group leaders work with parents within a collaborative model designed to be empowering and non-stigmatising. The group setting is considered important in helping parents to collaborate in problem solving and to feel less isolated in their parental role. Particular attention is paid to recruitment and retention of parents, including the provision of transport, day care, meals and flexible course times (Webster-Stratton, 1998a; Gardner et al, 2004). Research suggests that *The Incredible Years* programmes have proved themselves acceptable and effective with families from black and ethnic minorities in the US (Gross et al, 2003) and in the UK (Scott et al, 2001; Scott et al, 2006).

Staffing

Group leaders for the parent training programme can come from a variety of backgrounds including nursing, psychology, social work, psychiatry and education. They often possess masters or doctoral degrees in their discipline and a strong background in child development and counselling and have clinical experience with families. However, a strong training and accreditation process (outlined below) allows for group leaders to be qualified just to bachelor degree level. The most necessary requirement is comfort with the collaborative process needed with families, an ability to promote intimacy and friendship with families, and to be able to lead and teach (Webster-Stratton, 2001).

Training and accreditation

As part of its procedures to achieve programme fidelity, *The Incredible Years* organisation in the United States accredits group leaders in the UK, as well as certified mentors and trainers who are authorised to deliver the training for group leaders. Certified trainers are able to train counsellors, teachers and therapists and others to run the parent, teacher and child groups. Group leaders complete a certified training workshop, peer review, self-evaluation, video feedback and consultation lasting three days (Webster-Stratton, 2001).

Evidence

Numerous evaluations on both sides of the Atlantic using randomised controlled trials have shown *The Incredible Years* to be effective as a treatment in clinical settings with parents of conduct-disordered children (Webster-Stratton, 1984; Scott et al, 2001) and also when working preventively with parents of pre-school children from the wider community (Webster-Stratton 1998b; Gardner et al, 2004; Scott et al., 2006). An RCT conducted by Webster-Stratton and Hammond (1997) provided evidence of this. Families of 97 children aged 4-7 years-old with early-onset conduct problems were randomly assigned to one of four conditions; a parent-training group, a child-training group, a combined child and parent training group, or a 'waiting-list' control group. Post-intervention, all three treatment groups showed significant improvements compared to the control group in relation to child adjustment, mother observations of positive and negative behaviour, child conflict management skills and parent stress. One-year follow up assessments found continued improvement in parent and child behaviours and child conduct problems had also lessened. Webster-Stratton and Hammond (1997) concluded that the combined parent and child training group appeared to have the most positive effects in the broadest range of behaviours.

In Oxford in the UK, a 10-week Webster-Stratton parenting programme provided by trained health visitors for parents of 2 to 8-year olds achieved significant improvements at six-months in children's positive behaviour and reductions in conduct problems. Parents' levels of stress also fell significantly compared with a control group (Patterson et al, 2002). A later trial evaluating a 14-week programme with low-income families whose children had been referred for conduct problems had similarly positive results. Outcomes included reductions in child problem behaviours and increases in positive parenting, confidence and skill at six-months (Gardner et al., 2006). Another trial by Scott and colleagues (2006) made *The Incredible Years* available with a reading support programme (Supporting Parents on Kids Education – SPOKES) to an experimental group of parents of children aged 5 and 6 in a low-income neighbourhood of South London with a predominantly minority ethnic population. Positive results, compared with a control group, included increases in parents' sensitive responding to children, better use of effective discipline and decreased use of demeaning criticism. Parents from all ethnic groups improved equally. Direct observation of parent-child interation during play showed improvements in child attention and 'on-task' behaviour.

Another 'community' evaluation took place in North and Mid-Wales with more than 150 families of pre-school children using 11 Sure Start centres. An early paper by Hutchings and colleagues at the University of Wales, Bangor reported good results being maintained over six or more months after parents completed the BASIC course (Hutchings et al, 2006). The positive results included improvements in parenting skills and children's behaviour measured both by parents' reports and independent observation in the home. Attendance levels were good, with 86% of families in the experimental group attending at least half the 12 parenting sessions, and 100% reporting high levels of satisfaction. The initial effectiveness of *The Incredible Years* programme has been established across all the Sure Start neighbourhoods irrespective of local crime levels (Hutchings et al, 2006). A study of cost effectiveness is also being conducted as part of the evaluation.

Types of evaluation

Programme evaluations have included home and school observations by independent evaluators, and teacher and parent reports on standardised measures. Findings have been replicated across randomised studies by independent evaluators with different ethnic populations and age groups in the UK, Norway, US and Canada. Evaluation follow-up periods have extended from immediate post-programme completion to approximately three years, with the average around one year post-test. Many treatment effects remain significant for this duration.

The evaluators

The Incredible Years parenting programme has been evaluated by the programme developers and by independent evaluators in a range of different contexts and with diverse family groups.

Settings

The Incredible Years parenting programmes have achieved positive outcomes in several countries including England, Norway, Wales and the USA, with diverse family groups from disadvantaged communities including inner-city settings. The programmes have proved popular and effective with families from a range of different minority ethnic groups. In a US study, Reid et al (2001) found that improvements in child and parent outcomes were equally high amongst low-income families of White, African-American, Hispanic and South-East Asian ethnicity. This finding was supported by trials conducted in South London which included a large number of black and minority ethnic families (Scott, Spender et al, 2001; Scott et al, 2006). These findings make theoretical sense given the collaborative approach that encourages parents to set their own goals for their families and respects different viewpoints. In terms of place of delivery, the parent training programme can be implemented in a variety of settings including surgeries, schools, churches, mental health agencies, and public health centres. However, Scott and colleagues (2006) have used the results of their Primary Age Learning Study (PALS) in South London to argue that targeting *The Incredible Years* and other support services by geography alone may be a waste of resources. Despite high level of local poverty, most families taking part in the study were found to be thriving, without depression or measurable child behaviour problems.

Outcomes

Evaluation outcomes for the parent training programme have included: increased positive family communication and problem-solving, increased parent use of limit-setting, using non-violent discipline methods, reduced conduct problems in children's interactions with parents and increases in compliance to parent commands, increased parental involvement with school, reduced parental depression and increased self-confidence and increased positive emotional response (e.g. praise) and the decreased use of criticism, negative commands and harsh discipline.

In an assessment of what may mediate the effect of participation in the Incredible Years BASIC parent training programme, Webster-Stratton (1990) found significantly more children who post-intervention did not reach clinically normal scores had mothers who reported lower incomes, depression and alcoholism in their immediate families. These children were also more likely to have mothers who were single or divorced, indicating that marital distress may be important in terms of children's response to treatment (Webster-Stratton, 1990; Webster-Stratton, 2001).

Key messages concerning effectiveness

- Both programme developers and independent evaluators have rigorously evaluated *The Incredible Years* parenting programme with evidence of high effectiveness on a range of child and parent outcomes.

- The parent training programme helps parents strengthen their parenting skills and become more involved with their children's schooling with long-term effects.

- The parenting programme is acceptable and effective with parents from a range of different ethnic groups, including hard-to-reach and disadvantaged populations.

Triple P – the Positive Parenting Programme

Triple P is a multi-level, preventative parenting and family support strategy developed in Australia by Sanders and colleagues. The programme incorporates five levels of intervention strength ranging from universal services that any parent may find useful to targeted, clinical interventions for the families of children and adolescents with serious behavioural problems. Research into the system of behavioural family intervention that later became known as *Triple P*, began in 1977 with early findings published in the 1980s (Sanders, 1999).

Aims

Triple P seeks to enhance family protective factors and reduce risk factors associated with severe emotional, developmental and behavioural problems in children. Specifically, it aims to:
* augment the knowledge, skills and confidence of parents and increase their self-sufficiency and resourcefulness
* promote positive caring relationships between parents and their children in safe, engaging and non-violent environments
* promote children's social, emotional, intellectual, language and behavioural competencies through positive parenting (Sanders, 1999).

Developing parental capacity for self-regulation is a core tenet. Parents are equipped with the skills necessary to become self-sufficient in their parenting and to trust their own judgement to intervene with an appropriate method to deal with a particular problem. By encouraging parents to act in this way, *Triple P* contends that parents become more connected to social support networks around them (Sanders et al, 2003). It is also hypothesised that within a broader ecological context, increases in self-sufficiency are related to resilience in coping with adversity. Thus, the more self-sufficient parents are, the more likely they are to seek support when they need it, become involved in their children's education and protect their children from harm. This applies across all ecological contexts including families from different cultural backgrounds and those living in poverty or disadvantaged communities (Sanders et al, 2003).

Content

Triple P is designed to reach families with varying levels of support needs. The rationale for this approach is that children can have differing levels of dysfunction and parents have differing needs and preferences regarding the assistance they require. A tiered approach has the benefit of reducing unnecessary 'over-servicing' and ensuring the most efficient use of staff to support and promote competent parenting.

The content of the five levels of intervention becomes more intensive as the difficulties addressed become more severe.

- Level 1 is a universal, population-level campaign using TV and other media to provide brief information, raise community awareness of parenting issues, and to turn the process of learning about child behaviour into a normal, straightforward activity for parents. Emphasis is placed on self-directed action.
- Level 2 is targeted at parents with specific concerns about their child's behaviour or development. The majority of the intervention is self-directed by the parent, but specific advice is provided on tackling problem behaviour, via a personal or group consultation with a clinician, or by telephone.
- Level 3 is similar to the previous level but targets parents who also require consultations or active skills training to manage a particular behavioural or developmental problem.
- Level 4 is typically for parents of children with more severe behaviour problems who want intensive training in positive parenting skills. This is delivered by an programme focusing on parent-child interaction. Skills taught are in relation to the management of a broad range of target behaviours.
- Level 5 is characterised by intensive family intervention work for parents of children with concurrent behaviour problems who may, themselves, be experiencing depression, stress or conflict in the home. The content of this level includes an individually tailored programme. Modules can include mood management strategies, stress coping skills and home visits to increase parenting skills.

Implementation

Implementation techniques depend upon the level of intervention.

- Level 1 is designed as a universal prevention strategy targeting an entire population. A *Triple P* coordinator uses a media resource kit consisting of brief television and radio clips publicising the programme, newspaper columns on common parenting issues, information resources for parents such as tip sheets and videos, printed advertising materials including brochures and posters and a series of press releases and letters to editors and community leaders.
- Level 2 is implemented through primary care services who have

daily access to parents and children. For example, family doctors and schools who are seen as credible sources of information about children. Information can be obtained from these sources by parents without the stigma that may be associated with seeking help from specialist mental health services. The format of *Triple P* at this level is one or two sessions' intervention lasting usually 20 minutes in total, combined with tip sheets and videos containing basic information on prevention and management of common behavioural problems.

- Level 3 is implemented through primary care services, but taking place over three to four sessions and incorporating active skills training.

- Level 4 combines the skills training and other elements from Level 3 but teaches parents to apply parent skills to a broad range of target behaviours. There are three different delivery formats: *Standard* – includes a programme of ten sessions lasting up to 90 minutes each including modules on causes of behavioural problems, strategies for child development and managing misbehaviour. Home visits (lasting between 40-60 minutes) or clinic observation sessions are also conducted during which parents select goals to practise and feedback is given on observations of parent-child interaction. Further clinic sessions focus on identifying high-risk parenting situations and developing activity routines. Parents are additionally given maintenance and relapse sessions.
Group – includes an eight-session programme conducted in groups of 10-12 parents. There are four two-hour group sessions providing opportunities for parents to learn through observation, discussion, practice and feedback. Following this, there are three follow-up telephone sessions lasting 15-30 minutes to provide additional support, helping parents put into practice what they have learnt. The final session can take the form of a group or telephone session depending on the resources available.
Self-directed – occurs through the provision of detailed information in a parenting workbook outlining a 10-week self-help programme. This can be supported by weekly telephone consultations lasting 15-30 minutes. This package may be appropriate for use with families where access to clinical services is poor, for example in rural areas. But it obviously relies on self-motivation and a certain level of language and literacy ability.

- Level 5 can be implemented following participation in Level 4 if families request or are deemed to require further assistance. An initial session reviews progress and negotiates a treatment plan. Three enhanced individual therapy modules may then be offered, based on an clinical judgement and an assessment of family needs. Each module occurs over three sessions lasting up to 90 minutes. Parents are also engaged in an active skills training process and are offered feedback on their use of skills. Homework is completed between sessions to consolidate and apply learning. A final module at the end of the programme aims to promote maintenance of what has been learned.

Staffing

The staffing of *Triple P* reflects the strength of intervention. Levels 1, 2 and 3 are staffed by parent support or health promotion workers, including GPs, who may have routine contact with *Triple P* services and may be based in primary care services. Levels 4 and 5, requiring more intensive intervention, are provided by mental health and welfare staff and other allied health professionals.

Training and accreditation

There are a number of strategies for ensuring *Triple P* is faithfully implemented. Practitioners are licensed after taking part in standardised training and have to apply to a quality assurance process. 'Protocol adherence checklists' guide practitioners through the content of each session, and they are encouraged to join a peer support network to review cases and prepare for accreditation.

Evidence

The effectiveness of *Triple P* is evidenced by a series of randomised controlled trials in Australia that have evaluated it as both a community and clinical intervention (Sanders et al., 2000; Sanders, Markie-Dadds and Turner, 2003).

Sanders et al (2000) conducted a large-scale RCT comparing the three main variants of *Triple P* and waiting-list controls among 305 families of disruptive three-year-olds who were considered at high-risk of developing conduct problems. At post intervention, the parents who had been part of the self-directed or enhanced *Triple P* group reported significantly lower levels of disruptive behaviour, lower levels of dysfunctional parenting and greater parental competence than the other two groups. However, by one-year follow-up children in all three of the *Triple P* variants had achieved similar levels of clinically reliable change in disruptive behaviour. Findings from the study included a conclusion that enhanced service provision should be reserved for families who fail to make adequate progress after standard *Triple P* participation. They also indicated that self-directed programme variants could be as effective as more therapy based variants for some families.

The above findings were supported by Connell, Sanders and Markie-Dadds (1997) who conducted an RCT of self-directed variants of *Triple P* with 24 families living in rural areas, comparing them with a waiting list group. Again, the families contained a child aged 2 to 5 years-old at-risk of developing disruptive behaviour problems. Following intervention, families in the enhanced self-directed condition showed significantly lower levels of child disruptive behaviour. At post-intervention, all of the children in the waiting-list group, but only a third in the intervention condition were in the clinical range for disruptive behaviour. Another study examining the effectiveness of self-directed variants of *Triple P* with 63 pre-school children at risk of developing conduct problems produced similar results (Markie-Dadds & Sanders, 2006). Families were randomly assigned to either self-directed *Triple P* or a waiting list group. At post-intervention, parents in the self-directed programme used less coercive parenting practices and rated their children as having a significantly lower level of disruptive behaviour than children in the control group. There was, however, no difference between groups on measures of parental adjustment. Reports at the six-month follow-up stage indicated that gains in child behaviour and parenting practices had been maintained.

Sanders and McFarland (2000) conducted a further RCT of the enhanced *Triple P* programme. This assessed the effects of two forms of parent intervention in reducing mothers' depression and disruptive behaviour in families with a clinically-depressed parent and a child aged 3-9 who had already developed significant conduct problems (Sanders and McFarland, 2000). Forty-seven parents were randomly assigned to a standard behavioural family intervention or an enhanced condition. Both interventions were equally effective in reducing mothers' depression and child disruptive behaviour. However at six-month follow-up, more families in the enhanced condition had experienced a clinically reliable reduction in maternal depression and disruptive behaviour.

As yet there is limited evidence from independent RCTs of the cross-cultural applicability of *Triple P*, and no independent trials have yet been completed in Europe or North America. However, *Triple P* training courses have been introduced in Scotland (as part of the 'Starting Well' project) and England in recent years, leading to *Triple P* being offered in local areas. The programme is being implemented and evaluated in two areas of Glasgow, where a programme of intensive home-based health visiting has been established and group programmes have been introduced. Additionally, Manchester University are carrying out an evaluation supported by the Children's Fund of the universal, public-health based components of the programme.

Types of evaluation

Evidence on the effectiveness of *Triple P* as part of the broader context of research into behavioural family intervention is considerable, based on more than 20 RCT's of *Triple P* (Sanders, Markie-Dadds and Turner, 2003). Alongside the application of *Triple P* with families of children with disruptive behaviour disorders and oppositional defiant disorders the approach has been applied in other clinical contexts with success. These have included habit reversal in the treatment of thumb sucking (Christensen and Sanders, 1987), persistent feeding difficulties (Turner, Sanders and Wall, 1994), attention deficit hyperactivity disorder (Hoath and Sanders, 2002) and pain management (Devilly and Sanders, 1993; Sanders et al, 1996).

Triple P has been evaluated at all five levels of intervention and using different delivery modes within levels; this has included children of all eligible ages (birth-16 years old). Outcomes have been assessed in both clinical and community settings. Methods have included RCTs and other less rigorous methods. Follow-up evaluation periods have stretched from immediate post-intervention, and six-months to two years (with most treatment effects remaining).

The evaluators

The *Triple P* core programme has been developed by its originators through empirically-based research. Few evaluations of *Triple P* have been conducted by teams that are independent of the programme originators. However, evidence drawn from RCT's supports the view that the programme is effective in enhancing parental efficacy and competence and reducing disruptive behaviour and attentional difficulties in clinical and non-clinical populations (Moran, Ghate and van der Merwe, 2004).

Settings

Triple P has been shown through a series of RCTs to be effective with a range of family types and within different settings. The intervention has been used successfully by two-parent families, single parents, step-families, maternally depressed families, families experiencing marital discord, and families with a child with an intellectual disability (Sanders et al, 2003). Settings have included clinical and non-clinical settings in rural, remote and urban contexts.

Outcomes

Improved child behaviour and parental competence are the key outcome variables reported for all levels of *Triple P*. Benefits for parents have included greater confidence in their parenting ability, more positive attitudes towards their children, less reliance on potentially abusive parenting practices and parents are less depressed or stressed by their parenting role. Positive outcomes for children include experiencing fewer problems, getting on better with peers and being better behaved at school.

Key messages concerning effectiveness

- The multi-disciplinary approach and community-wide focus of *Triple P* gives the programme wide reach, including the opportunity to support families through primary care access points.

- The flexibility the programme can offer through different levels of intervention and its delivery methods are designed to increase participation and promote effectiveness. They also increase cost-effectiveness through better, more appropriate use of services.

- Success has been demonstrated in both clinical and non-clinical settings with a wide range of families types.

- Rigorous evidence is still needed from UK settings regarding *Triple P*'s effectiveness.

3 Home visiting programmes

Home visiting has a long history as an institutional means of reaching out to families who might not otherwise access health and social support services. In Britain, it dates back as far as Elizabethan times (Gomby et al., 1999), while the first health visiting service by nurses was introduced in the mid-19th century (Elkan et al, 2000). As a delivery mechanism, it embraces a wide range of professional, paraprofessional and voluntary services targeting different client groups, including older people as well as families and children. Their aims may vary between delivery of a parenting or health education curriculum to needs assessment, health screening or even monitoring for suspected abuse. Some services are specialised and highly targeted with narrow objectives, while others – notably Health Visitors under the National Health Service – provide services that are universally available to whole sections of the community and have multiple goals. (Gomby et al, 1993; Elkan et al, 2000).

On the boundaries of definable 'home visiting' one American programme for parents of adolescents has achieved promising results using booklets and follow-up phone calls by health educators to target under-age smoking and consumption of alcohol (Bauman et al, 2001). But in the context of long-term prevention of conduct disorders, criminality and their associated risks, most research interest has focused on home visiting for families with younger children, including ante- as well as post-natal support. As with group parenting programmes (Section 2), such interventions commonly include the promotion of established protective factors, such as parent-child bonding, even if there is no explicit acknowledgement of their relevance to preventing subsequent behaviour problems.

Evaluated interventions in Britain have included *The Child Development Programme* (CDP) (Barker & Anderson, 1988) which provides monthly home visiting for parents during the first two years of their child's life. Designed for use in different models, by Health Visitors or paraprofessional 'Community Parents', it equips visitors with cartoons and other user-friendly materials to share information on topics such as health, child development, diet and maternal wellbeing. There is an emphasis on empowering parents and helping them to devise reinforcement tasks between visits. An evaluation, where pairs of Health Visitors were randomly allocated to delivering the programme or providing their routine support service, found evidence of greater concentration and better social behaviour among children in homes where the CDP had been delivered (Barker & Anderson, 1988), as well as lower rates of child abuse (Barker, 1994). The analysis and reporting of data from the evaluation (and its appearance in non-peer reviewed publications) created some controversy, including disputed suggestions that some positive effects attributed to the CDP had been overstated (Stevenson, 1989; Barker and Anderson 1989). An independent evaluation of a CDP intervention for first-time parents in disadvantaged areas, subsequently compared retrospective and prospective samples of families in three neighbourhoods where the programme was implemented and four control neighbourhoods with similar socio-economic and demographic profiles (Emond et al, 2002). After applying statistical controls for 'clustering' differences between the intervention and control areas this found few statistically significant differences between mothers and their two-year olds who had participated in the 'First Parent Health Visitor Scheme' and conventional health visiting. However, a randomised controlled trial in Ireland of the paraprofessional 'Community Parents Programme' found that children whose parents had participated were more likely to have been breast-fed and received all their immunisations as infants than in families receiving conventional post-natal care; and that their mothers were less likely to say they felt tired and miserable (Johnson et al, 1993). Seven years later intervention children were more likely to use libraries regularly. Their mothers were more positive about their parenting, less likely to endorse physical punishment and more engaged in checking school homework (Johnson et al, 2000).

Another promising use of home visiting is the *Family Partnership Model* used in the UK to promote mental health among families where parents are under personal or relationship stress, or where children are showing early behaviour problems. The visiting 'Parent Advisers' are professionals trained in counselling skills and in parenting and behaviour management skills (Davis et al, 1997) An evaluation comparing 55 families with multiple problems who were visited with 38 similar families identified positive short-term benefits among the intervention group, including increased self-esteem and lower anxiety and depression, a better home environment for their children and apparent improvements in children's behaviour (Davis and Spurr, 1998). However, a controlled evaluation of the widespread Home-Start initiative in Britain, which uses trained volunteers as home visitors for families under stress, could find no significant short-term differences in different measures of wellbeing between 80 mothers visited during the first 11 months after giving birth and a comparison group of 82 similar families (McAuley et al, 2004). Despite the popularity of Home-Start among mothers, their improvements in self-esteem and reductions in stress levels and depressive symptoms were matched by the comparison group, as were improvements in their children's social and emotional development.

Internationally, as well as nationally, home visiting programmes whose impact on risk and protective factors for conduct problems has been robustly and positively evaluated are relatively scarce. A systematic review by Bilukha and colleagues (2005) identified four studies of early childhood home visiting that measured their impact on children's violent behaviour, only one of which yielded wholly positive and statistically significant results. The reviewers concluded there was insufficient evidence to declare home visiting effective in preventing child violence. However, the same review also assessed 21 different North American studies that reported findings on prevention of child maltreatment (mostly measured over follow-up periods of between 10 months and three years). The vast majority yielded positive results, leading the reviewers to conclude that programmes were capable of reducing reported abuse by well over a third (39%). It was also found that programmes led by professionals tended to produce greater effects than those delivered by paraprofessionals – although reviews with a less specific focus have concluded that vulnerable, 'hard-to-reach' mothers may actively prefer support from trained, experienced parents rather than professionals (Hodnett & Roberts, 2000; Barnes & Freude-Lagevardi, 2003).

A review by Gomby and colleagues (1999) of evaluations assessed two randomised controlled trials of home visiting where children's behavioural outcomes were assessed, of which only one – the *Nurse-Family Partnership* programme (Olds et al – see below) – produced significant, favourable effects. However, a meta-analysis of family-based intervention studies by Farrington and Welsh (2003) identified four evaluations of home visiting programmes with outcome measures of delinquency or antisocial behaviour whose methods equated to Levels 4 or 5 on the Scientific Methods Scale (Sherman et al., 1997. See above). These not only included the *Nurse-Family Partnership* programme but also a 5-year intervention in Western Australia by doctors 30 years ago (Cullen, 1976). The latter found reduced aggressive behaviour among young children around the time they began school. A shorter, post-natal visiting intervention (Stone, 1988) showed no significant impact on behaviour problems by the time children were aged 5 to 8.

In addition to evidence from specific 'home visiting' programmes it should be noted that home visits may be included as an element in two of the more intensive therapeutic interventions described below: *Functional Family Therapy* (FFT) and *Multi-systemic Therapy* (MST). Home visiting has also been a component in several multi-modal interventions that have demonstrated effectiveness in evaluations. These include the *High/Scope Perry Preschool Programme*, whose longitudinal evaluation of children randomly allocated to take part in an early years programme in the 1960s has identified multiple, cumulative benefits up to age 40 compared with a control group, including fewer criminal arrests (Schweinhart et al, 2005). Regular home visits were, likewise, an ingredient in three major longitudinal experiments with school-age children: the *Montreal Longitudinal-Experimental Study* (Tremblay et al, 1996) the Seattle Social Development Programme (Hawkins et al, 1999) and *Fast Track*, (Conduct Problems Prevention Study Group, 1999; 2002; 2006). The Montreal study combined anger management and social skills training for aggressive and hyperactive boys with family management skills training for their parents. The Seattle programme, working with a 'community' sample of elementary school children, combined parenting education with a cognitive and social skills programme for the children and classroom management training for their teachers. *Fast Track*, tested with 900 'antisocial' elementary school children in four US locations, added yet more preventive ingredients, including one-to-one academic tutoring and a peer friendship programme. The specific contribution of home visiting to the various positive outcomes reported for these programmes is, however, impossible to disaggregate.

The results when family-based home visiting is reviewed as a generic intervention for preventing behaviour problems can best be described as mixed. Gomby and colleagues (1999), in an overview of evaluations mostly published in the 1990s, found benefits were often concentrated among sub-groups of parents. Yet there was little consistency in subgroups across programme models, or even across sites implementing the same programme. In other words, home visiting programmes, even when implemented reasonably well, were unlikely to benefit all families. Positive results achieved by one model of home visiting did not necessarily apply to other models. The authors, accordingly, recommend that practitioners and policymakers should moderate their expectations for the success of programmes and pursue their development alongside other effective types of support service for families and children.

But if home visits are "not a silver bullet for all that ails families and children" (Gomby et al, 1999) it is still noticeable that one intervention, the *Nurse-Family Partnership* devised by Olds and colleagues (1997) has yielded evaluation findings that are more consistently positive. Information from randomised controlled trials on its content, implementation, effectiveness and its cost-effectiveness can be found below. Transplanting the programme from the United States to Britain raises interesting targeting, implementation and evaluation questions, not least the issue of 'dosage' in relation to the post-natal home visiting already provided by midwives and Health Visitors under the NHS. Nevertheless, the findings from America, relating to maternal as well as child behaviour and health, would seem fully to justify the UK Government's decision to pilot and then evaluate the programme in Britain.

Nurse-Family Partnership

Developed over a quarter of a century in America by David Olds and colleagues, the *Nurse-Family Partnership* is designed to help first-time mothers from low-income homes achieve the best start for their child and prevent health and parenting problems that can contribute to early antisocial behaviour. This is accomplished through intensive home visiting by trained nurses during pregnancy and the first two years after the child's birth. The programme has been evaluated and replicated in America with positive results indicating that it reduces the risks of children developing early antisocial behaviour and the later likelihood of juvenile offending.

Aims

The programme is designed to modify three important risk factors associated with the early development of antisocial behaviour:

* adverse health-related behaviour by mothers during pregnancy, including those associated with children's neurological deficits such as smoking, alcohol consumption and the use of illegal drugs
* child abuse and neglect
* a troubled maternal life course, including unintended subsequent pregnancies and reliance on state benefits (Olds, Hill and Rumsey, 1998).

Content

Nurse home visitors must follow detailed visit-by-visit guidelines. Risk factors are addressed by focusing on five domains of functioning listed by Olds (1998) as: personal health, environmental health, maternal role development, maternal life course development and family and friend support. Within each of these domains assessments are made of maternal, child and family functioning leading to specific targeted interventions. The guidelines by which home visits are structured are organised developmentally to reflect challenges as the pregnancy progresses and during the first two years of the child's life. The three main activities that take place are:

* promoting adaptive change in behaviour that can affect the outcomes of the pregnancy, the health and development of the child and the mother's future life course
* helping mothers to build supportive relationships with friends and family
* linking families into other services (Olds, 1998).

This occurs through the completion of worksheets; for example, exploring the mother's aspirations, teaching parenting skills (including better empathy and behavioural regulation of the child), setting goals regarding child care and personal health care, and closely monitoring diet, weight and smoking. The nurse also becomes involved in developing relationships with other family members to enhance the informal support available to the women. This occurs by asking the mother about other individuals and by observing their interactions. Where an adult relationship may be abusive, the nurse's role is not to actively intervene, but rather to show concern and respect and to communicate the belief that the women do not have to accept poor treatment and to help them make decisions that are in their best interests. Nurses also help reduce family stress by linking mothers to other formal services including housing, income support and other health services. The nurses encourage parents to keep child health care appointments and help them make best use of services available. With the mother's permission, this may include liaising with other health care staff.

Rigorous programme fidelity is seen as crucial to overall success (Olds, 1998; Olds et al, 2003) and the programme originators have expressed concern that the intervention will be 'watered down and compromised in the process of being scaled up' (Olds, 1998). While this may appear prescriptive nurse visitors exercise a high level of discretion within the structure regarding how to best meet the needs of the family with whom they are meeting. For example there may be a concerted focus on cessation techniques for an expectant mother who smokes.

Implementation

Programme implementation begins as soon as possible after the beginning of pregnancy and continues until the child's second birthday. During pregnancy, a nurse will visit the expectant mother at home on a weekly basis for the first month of enrolment then every other week until delivery. Following the birth, visits occur on a weekly basis for the first six weeks reducing to alternate weeks from six weeks to the child's 21st month. From then until 24 months, visits occur once a month. Visits last between 60-90 minutes.

The nurse home visitor is required to keep detailed records on the families' needs, the services provided, their progress and outcomes. To monitor programme fidelity, the programme originators have implemented a Clinical Information System (CIS) to record programme content, individual visits, and quality of implementation.

The basic structure of the programme being used, including caseload and target groups, is also examined (Olds, 1998).

Staffing

The *Nurse-Family Partnership* requires staffing by nurses chosen on the basis of their formal training in women's and children's health and their competence in managing clinical situations presented by at-risk families (Olds, 1998). A degree in nursing is regarded as beneficial as is experience in maternal, child or community nursing. However, a capacity for empathy and an ability to maintain appropriate boundaries is also seen as important. A full-time nurse home visitor can carry a caseload of 20-25 families.

Nurse home visitors require a Masters degree-level nursing supervisor to provide guidance, weekly individual supervision, case conferencing and oversight of programme implementation. The supervisor should have a background in maternal, child, community health or mental health nursing and have considerable experience of working with at-risk families.

It should be noted that the use of paraprofessionals to deliver the programme has been evaluated, although achieving fewer positive outcomes compared to using nurses (Olds et al, 2002 – see below).

Training and accreditation

Training is currently offered by the National Center for Children, Families and Communities (NCCFC) in Denver, Colorado before initiation of the programme. It begins with a one-week session for nurses and supervisors. This includes the history of the programme, its theoretical and empirical underpinning, stages in women's readiness for change, programme guidelines and record keeping. Following this initial session there are three-day and two-day follow up sessions, to coincide with nurses' use of the infant, then toddler, guidelines.

Evidence

A series of randomised controlled trials in the US have demonstrated the positive impact Nurse-Family Partnership can have on long-term outcomes for mothers and children. This effect has been most pronounced among poor, unmarried mothers and their children, but some impacts have also remained for less disadvantaged participants.

There have been three major trials. The first in semi-rural Elmira, New York (Olds et al, 1986) studied a sample of 400 women recruited during pregnancy (before 26 weeks gestation) and followed them through to their child's 15th birthday (Olds et al, 1997). Most of the women involved were white (89%), of low socio-economic status and teenaged when pregnant (none had previously had a live birth). The women were randomly assigned to one of four groups:

★ Treatment one – sensory and developmental screenings for the child at 12 and 24 months with further referral if deemed necessary

★ Treatment two – the same screenings plus free transportation to prenatal and well-child care through to the child's second birthday. Participants in treatments 'one' and 'two' made the same use of pre-natal and well-child care so were combined into a single comparison group for the analyses

★ Treatment three – families were provided with the screenings and free transportation but also received nurse visits at home during pregnancy

★ Treatment four – families received the same services as treatment three but the nurse continued to visit until the child's second birthday.

The women were interviewed during pregnancy and the first four years of their child's life. Other measures included reviews of medical and social records and home observation. At fifteen-year follow up, the children were interviewed and their school records reviewed to assess criminal and antisocial behaviour (Olds et al, 2003). This showed that women who experienced the full home visiting programme had better prenatal health behaviour and outcomes. They included a reduction in smoking and improved diet reducing the likelihood of neuro-developmental deficits for children (this was also significant for mothers in 'treatment three'). The women in 'treatment four' were also less likely to abuse or neglect their child during the first two years with significantly less abuse compared to other comparison groups by the child's 15th birthday. At fifteen-year follow up, the mothers in 'treatment four' reported a reduction in subsequent pregnancies, increased workforce participation and fewer months spent on welfare. They also had fewer arrests, fewer convictions, and fewer problems due to substance abuse than women in the control group. Among the 15-year old children of mothers who received nurse visits in pregnancy and the early years (treatment four), there were significant, positive effects on criminal and antisocial behaviour including 60% fewer instances of running away, 56% fewer arrests, 81% fewer convictions or violations of parole, 63% fewer lifetime sexual partners, 40% fewer cigarettes smoked per day, 56% fewer days of alcohol consumption, and 56% fewer parent reported behavioural problems due to the use of drugs and alcohol (Olds et al, 1998).

In the Elmira trial, the programme originators and evaluators were intensively involved in monitoring programme implementation. Moreover, the same team of nurses worked with the families for the entire duration of the programme. This highly-controlled environment meant the evaluation results most likely represented the best possible outcomes from the programme (Olds, 1998). In summary, it was found that prenatal and early infancy nurse visitation with low income, teenage, single mothers could increase protective factors and moderate risks associated with the later onset of children's conduct problems and reduce antisocial behaviour amongst children born into at-risk families (Eckenrode et al, 2001).

A second trial in Memphis was designed to look at the effects of the programme in a different population and urban setting (Kitzman et al, 1997, 2000). The programme began in 1990 and included a sample of 1,139 women of whom 92% were African-American, 97% unmarried, and 65% per aged 18 or younger. Unlike the previous trial, this was a study of effectiveness, testing the intervention in closer to real-life conditions. There was less involvement by the investigators in the administration of the programme and the trial was conducted during a nursing shortage. The women were randomly assigned to one of four treatment conditions:

★ Treatment one – free transport for prenatal care appointments
★ Treatment two – free transport for prenatal care plus developmental screening and referral services for the child at 6, 12, and 24 months of age
★ Treatment three – free transport and screening plus intensive nurse home visit services during pregnancy, followed by one post-partum visit in hospital and one post-partum visit in the home
★ Treatment four – services provided as in treatment three but with nurse visits continuing until the child's second birthday.

For analysis purposes, treatments 'one' and 'two' were combined to compare to treatments 'three' and 'four' for the prenatal phase. For the postnatal analysis, treatment two was compared to treatment four. As in Elmira, the measures used included regular maternal interviews, observation in the home and reviews of the mother and children's health and social service records. Follow-up occurred when the children were aged two (Kitzman et al, 1997) and then six (Kitzman et al, 2000, Olds *et al*, 2004a).

For the prenatal phase of the trial there were no differences in birth outcomes apart from a reduced likelihood of pregnancy-induced hypertension (Kitzman et al, 1997). This most likely related to epidemiological differences between the Elmira and Memphis samples and highlighted the need to understand different incidences of risk factors among different 'low-income' populations. Findings for postnatal outcomes for the first two years after delivery also indicated that the women who had received nurse home visits had fewer negative attitudes to child-rearing of a kind associated with abuse or neglect. Their children had fewer healthcare encounters resulting from injuries or ingestions. In addition, the mothers visited by nurses reported fewer second pregnancies than comparison group mothers. Their children were also observed to be more responsive and communicative to their mothers. This may relate to the training that mothers received from nurses on understanding their children, creating a greater level of sensitivity and responsiveness between mother and child. Some of these positive results persisted three years later (Kitzman et al, 2000) including fewer subsequent births for women previously receiving nurse home visits and less time spent on welfare. A lower percentage of six-year old children who had been nurse-visited were reported by their mothers to exhibit severe behavioural problems compared with control group children (1.8% versus 5.4%). They also demonstrated stronger intellectual functioning.

The third trial of *Nurse-Family Partnership* began in Denver, Colorado in 1994 and was designed to compare delivery of the programme by nurses and by paraprofessionals. In all, 735 pregnant women were recruited to the trial, 84% of whom were unmarried, and 45% if whom were American Mexican. The average age at registration was 19.8 years. All had no previous live births and were from low-income homes. The women were randomly assigned to one of three groups:

★ Treatment one – developmental screening and referral services for children at 12, 15, 21 and 24 months

★ Treatment two – the same screening and referral services as treatment two plus nurse home visits during pregnancy and for two years after birth

★ Treatment three – the same screening and referral services as treatment two plus paraprofessional home visits during pregnancy and for two years after birth.

Initial evaluation revealed differences in the nature and quantity of programme implementation between nurses and paraprofessionals (Korfmacher et al, 1999). Nurses carried out a higher number of visits from the child's birth to two years and spent more time on physical health and promoting child care compared to paraprofessionals. Paraprofessionals conducted longer visits and spent more time on the mother's life course development, other relationships, and health and safety compared to nurses. Follow up has so far occurred at two and four years from birth (Olds et al, 2002; Olds et al, 2004b). At two-year follow up the nurse-led implementation was shown to be of significantly greater benefit to maternal and child outcomes compared to the paraprofessional-led intervention or the control group. The single significant impact for the paraprofessional visited families was that mothers with low psychological resources had more responsive relationships with their children than control group counterparts. The four-year follow up again found no significant impact for the children of the paraprofessional visited families. However, significant findings were apparent for the mothers including that they were likely to have worked for longer periods, had better mental health and a greater a sense of mastery compared to their control group peers. The nurse-visited families continued to demonstrate positive impacts for both maternal and child outcomes.

Cost-benefit analyses show *Nurse-Family Partnership* in a favourable light compared to no intervention. Olds et al (1993, 1998) found that when the programme focused on low-income women, the costs of funding the programme were covered by the time the child was aged four; primarily due to the reduced number of subsequent pregnancies and a reduction in the use of welfare by the mother. A study carried out by the RAND Corporation (Karoly et al, 1998) found four types of significant saving resulting from application of the programme including: increased tax revenues from increased employment, decreased government assistance, for example welfare support, decreased expenditure for education, health and other services, and decreased criminal justice system spending. The analysts concluded that there were no savings to government when the intervention was carried out with low-risk families, but where the mother was living on a low-income and unmarried, savings exceeded the cost of the programme by a factor or 4:1 (Olds, 1998). This analysis was further supported by an independent cost-benefit analysis carried put by the Washington State Institute for Public Policy (Aos et al, 2004). This concluded that *Nurse-Family Partnership* ranked highest in terms of cost return among a range of programmes including pre-kindergarten, child welfare, youth development, mentoring, youth substance abuse prevention and teenage pregnancy prevention programmes. Calculations indicated that after implementation and benefit costs estimated at $35,416, the programme left a net return of $17,180 per family served or $2.88 per dollar invested. This analysis was based on the entire sample of the first randomised trial and may be increased for higher risk families. Cost savings do not however, include savings relating to reductions in subsequent pregnancies, pre-term births, child injury and immunisations, and welfare use.

Types of evaluation

The Olds model has been subject to three randomised controlled trials in the United States with random assignment to *Nurse-Family Partnership* and other treatments. Positive outcomes for low-income families have emerged immediately, and in follow-up studies at two, four, six and fifteen years later. The intervention has been subject to efficacy and effectiveness evaluations with positive results for both.

The evaluators

The programme developers have conducted the majority of the evaluations. Cost-benefit analyses have been undertaken by independent evaluators (Aos et al, 2004; Karoly et al, 1998).

Settings

All experimental evaluations of the Nurse-Family Partnership have so far occurred in the United States, in Elmira, New York; Memphis, Tennessee; and Denver, Colorado. These represent a small semi-rural setting, a major urban area and a metropolitan setting. The intervention has been targeted towards poor, unmarried, teenage mothers from White, African American and Hispanic populations but has also included evaluations of mothers in more advantageous circumstances who are not poor and are married.

Evaluations have included the use of nurses and paraprofessionals. In addition, a recent randomised controlled trial has sought to assess the impact of paraprofessional home-visiting among pregnant Native American adolescents (Barlow et al, 2006). Results indicate higher childcare knowledge among intervention mothers at two and six months compared to a control group, and higher maternal involvement at two months. No significant difference has been found for child care skills between the intervention and control groups.

Outcomes

Positive outcomes have been found for child development and for maternal life-course. Prenatal outcomes for mothers include improved diet, fewer kidney infections, greater informal support, greater use of community services, greater likelihood of employment, reduced smoking, fewer pre-term deliveries, and heavier babies at birth. Child development outcomes include less child abuse and neglect, fewer injuries and ingestions, fewer arrests by age 15, less running away and homes more conducive to positive child development.

Maternal life course outcomes include reductions in the number of subsequent pregnancies, increased participation in work, less time claiming welfare support, and increased spacing between first and second child.

Key messages concerning effectiveness

- The *Nurse-Family Partnership* programme in America has demonstrated effectiveness as an early-intervention strategy for mothers whose children are at risk of developing antisocial behaviour and engaging in later delinquency and juvenile offending

- It has proved especially effective (and cost-effective) as a pre- and post-natal support programme for teenage, single mothers and their children living in poverty

- The intervention appears to be more effective delivered by nurses, working to strict guidelines, than by trained paraprofessionals.

4 Multisystemic Therapy

Multisystemic Therapy (MST) is an intensive intervention that combines family and cognitive-behavioural therapy strategies with a range of other family support services. As the name implies, it views school, work, peers and the wider community as inter-connected systems that can influence the behaviour of individual young people and their families. Multiple problems associated with severe behaviour problems are seen as requiring multiple solutions. MST has principally been used with young offenders, including those involved in chronic, serious and violent crime, to provide an intensive community alternative to residential treatment and youth custody.

Aims

MST seeks to identify and target multiple factors that are contributing to a young people's behaviour problems. It primary goals are to:

* reduce young people's criminal activity
* reduce other types of antisocial behaviour such as drug misuse
* achieve better, cost-effective outcomes by reducing the need for custody and residential placements. (Henggeler, 1998; 2001).

The programme specifically aims to tackle factors contributing to young people's behaviour problems and poor family functioning through a range of formal and informal support in relevant settings. In particular to:

* improve discipline and supervision practices among parents and carers
* promote better family relationships and communications
* reduce young people's involvement with delinquent peers (and increase their association with pro-social peers)
* improve young people's performance in school
* involve young people in positive, pro-social leisure activities
* empower parents by enabling them to identify their own strengths

* establish informal support networks for parents among their extended families, neighbours and friends
* remove barriers that prevent families from accessing services. (Henggeler 1998 & 2001).

Content

Multisystemic Therapy was developed by Henggeler and colleagues at the University of South Carolina in the late 1970s and is designed for young people aged 10 to 17 who have severe behaviour problems, and their families. To achieve change in a young person's 'natural' environment, it uses a largely home-based delivery model. However, bespoke components are also delivered at school or in the wider community (Henggeler et al, 1998). To take an example suggested by the originators of the programme, a 15-year old boy's persistent aggression and criminal activities might variously relate to involvement with delinquent peers, underachievement and disruptive behaviour in school, having a socially-isolated mother who is clinically depressed and whose parenting skills are poor and living in neighbourhood lacking constructive activities for young people (Henggeler et al, 1995). Multisystemic treatment might, therefore, begin by treating the mother's depression, providing training in parenting skills and helping to create a network of support among neighbours and friends. Progress would allow families to take the lead in setting new treatment goals – such as strategies to improve parental monitoring and discipline and draw the young person away from delinquent peers. Many of the families that have participated in MST in the United States have been ordered to do so by the courts. The programme providers argue that the court order is helpful in allowing the therapists to get 'a foot in the door', but has little other impact (Henggeler, 1998; 2001).

Implementation

Therapists typically work with four to six families at a time and are on call 24 hours a day. Services are often provided at weekends and during evenings to promote family attendance. The average duration of treatment is around 60-hours of contact time spread over four months. Initial assessment sessions investigate strengths and weaknesses of the focus young person, his/her immediate family and their connections with outside 'systems' including peers, school and the parental workplace. Friends, teachers, neighbours and extended families may be interviewed to obtain 'multiple and independent views'. The family and therapist agree together which problems will be targeted and how positive changes can be achieved. Interventions typically include a parenting component, including monitoring, rewards, sanctions and discipline, communications and shared problem-solving. They also normally include efforts to establish better communications and a collaborative relationship between parents and the young person's school (Henggeler, 1998; 2001).

The timing and length of MST sessions are determined by the family's needs. Individual sessions may last between 15 minutes and over an hour. They are often held daily in the early stages of treatment, or when there are signs that progress has stalled. In mid-treatment there may be two or three sessions per week (plus telephone calls from the therapist) declining to one session a week towards the end of treatment. As a core principle of MST, all interventions are designed to require daily or weekly effort from the young person and other family members. Performance of the previously agreed 'tasks' is the first agenda item for any session.

Staffing

Teams consist of three practitioner/therapists qualified to post-graduate degree level (who may be social workers, psychologists or youth justice staff), plus a supervisor (usually a clinical psychologist). Each team can provide services for around 50 families a year. The team needs a wide range of skills, including cognitive behavioural therapy, systemic family therapy, marital therapy, problem solving skills and anger management training. Staff undergo weekly supervision and training. The need for staff to be expert in a range of different modalities has been identified as a particular challenge since it can be difficult to achieve in routine practice.

Training and accreditation

Training for MST staff is provided by Multisystemic Therapy Services Inc in Charleston, South Carolina. Therapists and supervisors receive:

* five days of intensive training (administrators and stakeholders from collaborating agencies are also invited to the first, introductory day)
* 1.5 day booster sessions on a quarterly basis (focusing on specialist topics, such as parental drug misuse)
* weekly telephone consultations with MST experts (designed to achieve quality control and programme fidelity, as well as addressing specific, clinical problems).

Other elements of MST's quality assurance system include manuals for the programme's key components and a standard questionnaire for obtaining feedback from parents and carers.

Evidence

MST has been subject to several RCTs and has a relatively robust evidence base (Littell, Popa & Forsythe, 2005). Results show it to be an especially promising intervention for adolescents with conduct disorders, including violent and chronic young offenders, in both the short and long-term (2 to 5 years). MST has been shown to decrease problem behaviours, particularly aggression and delinquency, improve family relations, decrease association with deviant peers and lower re-arrest rates and time spent in institutions. A review by Curtis, Ronan and Borduin (2004) found that young people and their families treated with MST were functioning better and offending less compared to 70% of their counterparts who received alternative treatment or services. Analyses additionally suggest that MST is a cost-effective intervention (Henggeler 1997; Henggeler et al, 1998) despite high treatment costs. Early work by Schoenwald et al (1996) suggested that the incremental costs of MST were nearly offset by just the savings on days spent by substance misusing adolescent offenders in out-of-home placements.

Three significant controlled trials of MST were conducted in America in the 1990s in relation to violent and chronic juvenile offenders. The first conducted by Henggeler, Melton and Smith (1992) in South Carolina involved 84 violent and chronic young offenders (average age 15.2 years) at imminent risk of out-of-home placement and their families who had multiple needs. More than half the sample were African-American and three-quarters were male. The young people and their families were randomly assigned to either MST or the usual services provide by the Department of Juvenile Justice. At 59-weeks following intervention, the young offenders who received MST self-reported less criminal activity, had fewer arrests and had spent 73 fewer days in custody on average than their counterparts who had received the usual services. Families of the young offenders experiencing MST also reported increased family cohesion (in the 'usual service' condition, family cohesion decreased) and less aggression in relations between the young person and peers. These treatment gains remained at longer-term (2.4 years) follow up. Relative effectiveness was not moderated by taking account of demographic characteristics or psychosocial variables, indicating that MST was equally effective with young people and families of divergent backgrounds.

A further evaluation of MST by Borduin et al (1995) occurred in Missouri with 176 chronic juvenile offenders, also showing positive outcomes. The study examined the long-term effects of MST compared with individual therapy (IT). MST was found to decrease behaviour problems and improve family relations at post-treatment. Four-year post-treatment data showed that young offenders who had received MST were arrested less often and for less serious crimes than their counterparts who had received IT. Recidivism rates were 22% for MST participants, 72% for IT recipients and 87% for similar young offenders who had refused to participate in either MST or IT. Arrest and incarceration data obtained on average 13.7 years after treatment supports this (Schaeffer and Borduin, 2005). Although recidivism rates among former MST participants (including treatment dropouts) had risen to 50%, this was still substantially and significantly lower than the 81% who had participated in individual therapy. MST participants had 54% fewer arrests and an average 57% fewer days in custody. This latest follow-up is the longest to date for any clinical trial using MST with serious juvenile offenders. It provides evidence of relative effectiveness extending into adulthood with young people whose multiple arrests before the age of 14 suggest they were potential 'life-course persistent' (Moffitt, 1993) offenders.

The third RCT was conducted by Henggeler et al (1997) at multiple sites in South Carolina. The evaluation examined the role of treatment fidelity in the successful dissemination of MST. In all, 155 youths and their families were randomly assigned to either MST or the usual juvenile services available. Unlike previous trials, MST experts were not significantly involved in treatment implementation and quality assurance. Treatment effect sizes were found to be smaller than those in previous studies. This was especially true of decreased criminal activity, although days in custody were still lower by 47% at 18 months follow-up compared with the control group. The analysis also indicated that outcomes were considerably better in cases where the level of adherence to the programme by parents, adolescents and therapists was high. This highlighted the importance of maintaining treatment fidelity when disseminating family-based services to community settings.

Findings from a randomised trial, that took place across multiple sites in Norway (Ogden and Halliday-Boykins, 2004) reinforce these results. The trial provided an opportunity for an independent evaluation of the effectiveness of MST in treating adolescent anti-school behaviour in a community setting outside America. One hundred seriously antisocial youths were randomly assigned to MST or to 'usual' Child Welfare Services. In the short-term (six months), MST was found to reduce youth anxiety and aggression, reduce out-of-home placements and increase social competence. Many of these positive effects remained at two-year follow-up, with MST shown to be more effective than the usual service in reducing out of home placement and behavioural problems (Ogden and Hagen, 2006). Supporting the importance that the originators place on faithful implementation (Henggeler et al, 1997) the Norwegian study also found that the site where adherence to MST protocols was most problematic delivered the least good outcomes. A further point, highlighted in the review by Curtis et al (2004) is that the average positive effects of MST have been larger when the programme has been delivered by graduate therapists as opposed to therapists from the community.

Types of evaluation

MST has been subject to rigorous evaluation and replication in clinical and community settings in the United States, Canada and Norway. Most of the evaluations of MST have been RCTs and have covered a wide range of groups. For the purpose of this review, evidence is included in direct relation to juvenile justice outcomes with young offenders; but it should be noted that considerable evidence has also been gathered concerning benefits in relation to substance use preventions (Henggeler et al, 2002), sex offending (Borduin & Schaeffer, 2001), mental health (Santos et al, 1995; Huey et al, 2004), maltreating families (Brunk et al, 1987) and paediatric health (Ellis et al, 2005). Evaluation follow-up periods have stretched from immediate post-treatment to five and 13.7 years with most lasting more than a year. The indications are that many of the positive treatment effects identified have proved enduring.

However, a recent systematic review by Littell et al (2005) questions MSTs 'well-established' effectiveness. Littell et al's review notably differs from other reviews in its emphasis on Intent to Treat (ITT) analyses. This takes account of outcomes among programme dropouts and 'refusers' who tend to have more negative outcomes than those who participate in the programme. On this basis, Littell et al found when the results of the eight RCTs were pooled there was no significant difference between MST and usual juvenile justice services (although substantial heterogeneity indicated that different studies came to different conclusions). Even so, Littell et al recognised that MST has several advantages over other services including its comprehensiveness, and its basis in current knowledge and theory about the problems young people and their families face. MST has been studied more than many other services available for troubled youth and there is no available evidence to suggest that any other intensive intervention is more effective.

The evaluators

Many of the evaluations to date have been conducted by MST's originators. As Curtis et al (2004) suggest it is possible that the MST developers acting as clinical supervisors in the efficacy studies contributed to higher effect sizes compared to other effectiveness studies. Two independent trials have taken place, but with differing results. The first independent study took place in Canada (Leschied & Cunningham, 2002). The four-year randomised evaluation took place in four Ontario communities with approximately 400 families, 200 of which received MST, with the rest receiving 'usual services' through local youth justice and social service systems. Interim results found no significant treatment effects. This led the evaluators to conclude that either the treatment effect was too small to be detected with the sample size; or that there was no treatment effect that exceeds that of the usual services provided in Ontario; or that both the treatment and control services are effective in reducing criminal convictions; or, that MST might have been more effective in Canada under different implementation conditions, with different clients, different outcomes measures or compared to different services. However, the other independent RCT, conducted in the United States, did find positive outcomes, including a significant reduction in re-arrest rates at 18-months for young people who had received MST compared to treatment as usual (Timmons-Mitchell et al, 2006).

Settings

Whilst many of the evaluations have been confined to a US setting, MST has been successfully implemented in both urban and rural contexts. Settings have also included both clinical and community contexts. Recent evaluations have also taken place in Norway and Canada, although the latter found no treatment effect (see above).

Outcomes

Evaluations of MST have identified improved family relations, decreased behavioural problems, decreased association with deviant peers, reduced criminal offending including reduced violent crime, reduced substance misuse, decreased out-of-home placements, decreased recidivism, decreased days spent in custody, increased school attendance. Significant decreases in antisocial behaviour and criminality among young people with serious, early-onset offending records appear to have been maintained in the short and longer-term, extending into adulthood.

Key messages concerning effectiveness

- MST is a promising intervention for treating young people with conduct disorders, especially those who have been active offenders from an early age (although further independent trials in a European context are needed).

- The programme's relative effectiveness appears related to its emphasis on tailored intervention in the community to tackle a combination of individual, family and environmental risk factors.

- Relative effectiveness is not moderated by demographic characteristics or psychosocial variables. This indicates that MST is equally effective with young people and families from divergent backgrounds.

- Programme fidelity is crucial to achieving maximum positive effects. This is likely to be assisted by use of graduate-level therapists.

5 Therapeutic or Treatment Foster Care

Therapeutic Foster Care – or Treatment Foster Care – has evolved since the early 1950's as an alternative to residential care or custody for children and young people with serious behavioural problems, especially those involved in chronic and serious offending. The potential benefits of placing troubled and troublesome adolescents with skilled foster carers were underlined by a review of more than 40 outcome studies which concluded that long-term placements achieved significant improvements in social skills (Reddy & Pfeifer, 1997).

Therapeutic fostering has become widespread in the United States and in Britain there have been examples for more than 20 years of 'Community Support Schemes' providing foster homes for serious or persistent young offenders on bail, although none have been evaluated using a comparison design or control group (Utting, 1996). However, in 2005 the Department for Education and Skills made funds available to Councils with Social Services Responsibilities through a competitive bidding process to establish schemes that replicate the *Multi-dimensional Treatment Foster Care* (MTFC) programme developed by Patricia Chamberlain and colleagues at the Oregon Social Learning Center (OLSC) in 1983. MTFC is the most widely cited example of TFC and most rigorously evaluated. The initiative spearheaded by the DfES will also be subject to a rigorous evaluation either by RCT or similar method. A National Treatment Foster Care Team based at the Maudsley Hospital in London and Booth Hall Children's Hospital in Manchester has been established in an attempt to ensure programme fidelity and address other implementation issues through developmental support, training and consultation.

Multidimensional Treatment Foster Care (MTFC)

As its origins with the Oregon Social Learning Center imply, the Multidimensional Treatment Foster Care draws on the same theory and principles of social learning as the Parent Management Training interventions previously described in this report. Foster parents are recruited, trained and receive professional support in providing family placements for children and young people with serious behaviour problems. The programme is 'multidimensional' through its incorporation of a number of different methods of working. For example, it embraces individual therapy, family therapy and close monitoring by foster carers in the home and school, so that different problems can be addressed simultaneously and different learning styles can be accommodated.

Aims

The programme aims to reduce problem behaviour and promote more positive, normative and age-appropriate behaviour through:

* close monitoring and supervision at home, at school and in the community
* setting rules and boundaries that are clear, fair and consistently applied (backed by a 'points' system for acceptable and unacceptable behaviour)
* predictable consequences when rules are broken
* a supportive mentoring relationship with foster carer(s)
* minimal association with friends and peers with behaviour problems.
* individualised programming adjusted to fit the young person's changing needs and progress (Chamberlain, 1998).

Content

Children and young people are placed singly with their foster families for between six to nine months. In addition to behavioural parent training and support for the foster parents, MTFC provides:

* family therapy and aftercare groups for the young person's own parents, or carers
* skills training and supportive therapy for the young person
* behavioural interventions and support for learning at school
* psychiatric consultation and medication management when required.

Implementation

Foster parents are salaried and receive approximately 20 hours of pre-service training. During placements they can call on programme staff in a crisis at any time of the day or night for back-up and advice. They take part in group support meetings with other parents on a weekly basis and are contacted by staff each weekday for a Parent Daily Report. The originators of the programme view this as a good way to not only monitor the child or young person's progress, but also ensure the quality of implementation. Without routine consultation the organisers anticipate that typically high levels of negative and non-compliant behaviour would rapidly lead to foster parents responding in a 'non-theraputetic' ways (Chamberlain, 1998).

Young people take part in a structured behaviour management pro-gramme implemented in their foster home. They also take part in weekly therapy sessions with an individual therapists. School atten-dance, homework completion and behaviour are closely monitored by their carers (Chamberlain, 1998).

Family therapy is provided for the young person's own family with the intention that they will eventually return home. It is also provided during aftercare, once the young person has returned home. Parents are taught to use the same structured systems that are used in the fos-ter home and they are encouraged to maintain frequent contact with their child and the MTFC case manager. Home visits can begin usu-ally three weeks after initial placement to reinforce the intention that the family should become part of the treatment team and to enable the parents to practise and refine specific parenting skills.

Staffing

TFC Consultants Inc (an offshoot company that promotes and pro-vides training, accreditation and technical support) estimate that to operate a program with approximately 10 placements (a typical start-up size) requires:

* one foster family for each placement
* a full-time program supervisor
* half-time individual therapist or hourly playgroup staff for the pre-school programme
* half-time family therapist
* skills trainer(s) at approximately 20 hours a week
* .75 FTE foster parent recruiter, trainer, and daily report caller
* psychiatrist services on an hourly fee basis.

Training and accreditation

TFC Consultants Inc. supports three different versions of MTFC designed for; pre-school children; 6 to 11-year olds; and adolescents aged 12 to 18. Accreditation is only currently available for the latter two models.

Training and technical support requirements specified as part of the accreditation process include an initial site visit by TFC Consultants and a four-day training session for programme staff. A two-day training is also provided for the first foster parents. Monitoring of implementation is carried out using the internet, by weekly phone contact and through completion of quarterly reports. Certification, which includes a requirement for videotaping of foster parent and clinical staff meetings, is provided independently by the Center for Research to Practice, also based in Eugene, Oregon.

Evidence

The limited number of rigorous evaluations of the Oregon Social Learning Center (OSLC) model of MTFC that have taken place have been encouraging. The results from these suggest that MTFC leads to better outcomes for children and families and is cost effective compared to other community-based treatment models.

Using a matched comparison design, with young male and female offenders aged 12-18 years old, Chamberlain (1990) compared the rates of incarceration for 16 MTFC participants with adolescents who received treatment on other community programmes. A higher proportion of the MTFC participants completed their six-month programme placement and significantly fewer were likely to be in custody in the first two years after treatment than their comparison group. Chamberlain estimated that the saving in terms of the reduced number of days spent in custody equalled $122,000 over a two-year period (with incarceration costs estimated at $100 per day).

The most comprehensive evaluation of the OSLC model of MTFC was conducted by Chamberlain and Reid (1998) in an RCT that examined process and outcome variables. A total of 79 male participants aged 12-17 referred through the juvenile justice system with histories of serious and chronic delinquency were randomly allocated to either MTFC or Group Care (GC). The latter treatment involved the boys living in homes with six to 15 others who had similar histories of delinquency. The homes were staffed by shift workers and used a positive peer culture approach in which boys participated in group work and the establishment of discipline and decision-making rules. MTFC participants were placed in foster families with close supervision, and clear rules and consequences for breaking them. These boys attended school everyday and were monitored on their attendance, homework completion and attitude. In addition they attended weekly family therapy sessions. Results at the three-month, six-month and one year follow up found that MTFC produced more favourable outcomes than Group Care, possibly due in part to the separation of the MFTC treatment boys from delinquent peers. Boys participating in MTFC ran away less often (31% v 58%), completed their programmes more often (73% v 36%) and were locked up in detention or training schools less frequently and for less time (53 v 129 mean days) than their GC counterparts. MTFC boys also had fewer criminal referrals than boys in GC following the year after programme discharge. They reported that they had committed fewer delinquent acts, and fewer violent and serious crimes. The two-year follow-up had similarly positive results for MTFC (Eddy et al, 2004) with only 5% of participants having two or more criminal referrals for violent offences compared to 24% of young people who had taken part in GC. Rates of self-reported violence were also considerably lower.

Following up an aspect of this earlier study, Leve and Chamberlain (2005) examined data from two randomised intervention trials (one male sample and one female sample) with delinquent adolescents placed either in MTFC or GC to examine process variables. The findings suggested that MTFC was significantly better than GC in reducing adolescents' delinquent peer association measured at 12-month follow-up.

In an earlier study, Chamberlain, Moreland and Reid (1992) evaluated the impact of weekly foster parent groups on placement disruption rates for children aged four to seven in foster care. Seventy-two foster families were randomly assigned to one of three groups; enhanced support including weekly group meetings where they were taught a version of the MTFC individualised programme, received telephone calls three times a week from the group facilitator to 'troubleshoot' problems and received an increased payment of $70 per month (31); increased payment only (14); or, foster care 'as usual' (27) (with neither the enhanced training nor increased payment). Child outcomes included significantly fewer failed placements and significantly fewer disrupted days for the children in the enhanced group compared to the other treatment condition. This group also showed the largest drop in problem behaviours after three months. Foster parents in the enhanced programme were also almost two-thirds less likely to drop-out of fostering.

The effectiveness of MTFC has also be been evaluated in relation to the child and adolescent mental health system in America specifically in relation to 20 male and female children and adolescents aged 9-18 leaving an Oregon State Mental Hospital (Chamberlain and Reid, 1991). Within this study the effectiveness of MTFC was compared to a typical community treatment with good results including quicker placement in a family setting and adult reports of better daily rates of child problem behaviours.

Types of evaluation

The OSLC model of MTFC has been subject to a small number of quasi-experimental evaluations and trials that included random assignment to MTFC and other treatments. Follow up of evaluation outcomes has been between immediate post-intervention to two years, with treatment effects present across this time frame. Recommendations concerning TFC as a promising approach have largely relied on the MFTC literature. Evaluations of wider applications of TFC, although lacking equivalent rigour, offer some support for the benefits of TFC for both children and foster parents; for example in placement permanency, improvement of social skills and reductions in behavioural problems (Reddy & Pfeiffer, 1997).

The evaluators

Evaluators have used rigorous study designs to examine the impact of MTFC on young people involved in the juvenile justice and mental health systems. However, many of the evaluations have been carried out by those involved in the original design of the programme. There is a current lack of independent evaluations.

Settings

MTFC has been successfully used with a range of young people, including those with severe emotional and behavioural problems, histories of abuse and neglect, inappropriate sexual and aggressive behaviour, antisocial behaviour and delinquency, mental health problems, juvenile offending and youths with borderline intellectual functioning. There is, however, a need for further research to determine the populations for whom MTFC is effective and under what conditions. The strength of MTFC lies in its community-focused approach involving the home, school, police and other systems with which the young person interacts and evaluations have, accordingly been community-based.

Some providers of TFC have developed culturally-adapted models for use in specific communities. One example of this was the In-Care

Network in Montana, which developed a TFC intervention for Native American youth building on cultural and historical traditions such as the inclusion of extended kin (Potter & Mulkern, 2004).

Outcomes

Research has identified more rapid improvements in children's behaviour, decreased levels of aggressive and/or delinquent behaviour, good levels of subsequent homing in more lenient and less-restrictive settings and increased placement stability. Other positive outcomes include: lower re-arrest rates, less engagement in risky behaviour such as unprotected sex and drug use, better family relationships and functioning, better emotional regulation, fewer developmental delays.

Key messages concerning effectiveness

- The Oregon Social Learning Center model of MTFC appears to be a successful and relatively cost-effective intervention with male and female children 'at risk' and with adolescents involved with the youth justice and mental health systems.

- Full support and training is required for foster parents to achieve acceptable retention rates and stability for the children concerned.

- One of the strengths of MTFC for young offenders is the time young people spend away from delinquent peers in a structured and individualised care setting

6 Functional Family Therapy

Functional Family Therapy (FFT) is a multisystemic family intervention programme for young people aged 11 to 18. FFT has been developed in the United States over more than 30 years to add clinical features and improve outcomes in the diverse communities in which it has been implemented (Alexander & Parsons, 1973; Sexton & Alexander, 2000). The programme is targeted at young people deemed 'at-risk' of developing delinquent behaviour and at a more intensive level for young people already involved in serious, chronic criminal behaviour. FFT has been applied successfully in a variety of multi-ethnic, multicultural contexts to treat a range of high-risk youths and their families.

Aims

Working with the families of delinquent children/adolescents, FFT aims to:

★ reduce defensive communication patterns
★ increase supportive interactions
★ promote supervision and effective discipline (Brosnan & Carr, 2000).

Content

FFT has in recent years been refined to comprise three phases of intervention, as described below (Sexton & Alexander, 1999). Each phase has clear goals and assessment objectives, addressing different risk and protective factors and calling for particular skills from the treatment provider at each stage (Sexton & Alexander, 2000).

Phase 1: Engagement and motivation

During this initial phase, FFT focuses on applying re-attribution techniques to address and change maladaptive perceptions, beliefs and emotions. From this, it is expected that the family will begin to perceive that change is possible, and reduce resistance and negativity, while increasing alliance and trust with the therapist and respect for individual differences and values.

Phase 2: Behaviour change

The FFT clinicians begin to develop and apply the behaviour change plans that will ultimately yield intermediate and long-term results. The plans are formulated to be culturally appropriate and context-specific to individuals and their families. Assessments include cognitive, interactive and emotional components. These are designed to support attributional processes and coping strategies, while increasing understanding of behaviour, aiding the reinforcement of positive aspects and preventing blame and negativity. The therapist's role is to provide concrete behavioural intervention that guides and models specific behaviour changes. This may include suggested parenting techniques, as well as communication and conflict management strategies.

Phase 3: Generalisation

This phase focuses on enabling the family to apply the techniques and skills they have learnt to other problem areas or situations. Support for long-term change is given by linking the families with community resources and services.

Implementation

The intervention consists of 8-12 hours of direct service extending to 26-30 hours for more serious cases. It is delivered over a three-month period. Sessions can be conducted in clinical settings as an outpatient therapy or through home visiting. Each phase has its own assessment process and model adherence procedures. Outcomes are monitored from therapist and family perspectives by the frequent completion of progress notes and questionnaires (Lane et al, 2004).

A systematic approach to training and programme implementation has been implemented in recent years and a comprehensive system for client, process and outcome assessment has been added. This latter component is aided by a computer-based client tracking and monitoring system (FFT-CSS). This has helped clinicians identify and implement goals for therapeutic change in a clear and accountable manner and promoted programme fidelity (Alexander et al, 1998).

Staffing

FFT is described as a relatively low-cost treatment that can be administered by lower-cost professionals (Alexander et al, 1998). Therapists implementing FFT should have a Masters level degree in a related area e.g. psychology, counselling, marriage and family therapy etc. and should be well-grounded in the theoretical tenets of FFT, including a willingness and ability to maintain therapeutic focus, multicultural sensitivity and persistence. The originators suggest that non-Masters level therapists may administer FFT if closely supervised by a Masters level clinician.

Training and accreditation

Implementing FFT requires a 'site' to follow a systematic process, taking about one year to complete. Sites are working groups of FFT professionals who staff cases together. A core agreement of any site wishing to implement FFT is that they agree to allow FFT therapists to meet regularly, have at least a half-time case load e.g. five to eight families at any one time (full-time FFT therapists can manage on average 64 cases a year), and allow time to undertake FFT supervision and consultation. Site certification requires all of the following components:

* initial three-day clinical training
* clinical FFT externship for one member of staff (this person will normally then become the clinical lead for the site working group)
* follow-up training and supervision comprising three visits per year of two days duration each
* supervision consultations with FFT supervisors; these total four hours per month for the first two years of implementation
* use of all elements of the FFT family assessment protocol and computer tracking system (FFT-CSS) (Alexander et al, 1998).

There are four levels of certification each requiring a different type and degree of training and supervision. Certification is restricted to completion of officially sanctioned FFT training courses.

* *Functional family therapist* – this requires completion of a one-year training programme including initial clinical training, monthly supervision and three follow-up training courses with one subsequent year.
* *FFT clinical team leader* – this involves the completion of level one and successful completion of an Externship in FFT. Qualified individuals can lead the implementation and practice of FFT at a certified FFT site.
* *FFT clinical supervisor* – this requires completion of levels 1 and 2 and completion of an FFT course on supervision. The clinical supervisor also receives supervision from another certified clinical supervisor. Successful completion of this level means that

the individual can then take responsibility for the cases of other FFT therapists and provide group and individual supervision within their agency and externally.

★ *FFT trainer* - to achieve this level, completion of all other levels is necessary with additional completion of a course on delivering FFT training. Any training provided by this individual must be sanctioned by FFT.

To continue to act as an approved FFT site, the organisation must organise (approved) on-site training at least once a year and at least one telephone consultation per trained staff.

Evidence

Evidence from randomised and non-randomised comparison trials of efficacy and outcome measures conducted in the US over the last 30 years indicates that FFT is successful in reducing recidivism in juvenile delinquents and chronic juvenile offenders. It has also pointed towards some relevant findings concerning implementation, such as the use of paraprofessionals. Analysis of costs would also suggest that FFT can make significant savings compared to residential care or incarceration (Sexton & Alexander, 2000). Sexton and Alexander (2000) estimated that on average clinic-based FFT treatment (12 sessions) cost $700-1000 per family, compared to the average cost of detention per adolescent that equated to $6,000 for 90 days. The average cost of a residential programme in the area under study was $13,500 for 90 days with a three-year recidivism rate of 90% compared to FFT 1-year recidivism rate of 19.8%.

One of the first outcome evaluations of FFT was by Alexander and Parsons (1973). In this study, 99 court-referred juvenile delinquent adolescents' aged 13-16 years-old were randomly assigned to either FFT or one of three other conditions including a no-treatment control group, a client-centred family therapy group or an eclectic psychodynamic family therapy group. The adolescents were predominantly white, living in a moderate-sized city and were of lower to middle SES. They received approximately 10 weeks of therapy provided in a clinic by first and second-year graduate students in psychology who had undergone FFT training and supervision. At follow-up (6-18 months) the adolescents who had received FFT had a considerably lower re-offending rate (26%) compared to the other conditions (range from 47-73%). Post-intervention court referrals were also lower and family interactions had improved, as had communication skills for the FFT families. In subsequent follow-ups, at 2.5 and 3.5 years the researchers found that the siblings in the families had a lower rate of court referral than siblings in other conditions: 20% compared to 40-63%. This was linked to differentiated family process within the families who had received FFT compared to other conditions (Klein et al, 1977).

A later study by Barton et al (1985) comparing 27 young delinquents who had received FFT found similar results to Alexander and Parsons (1973). Again, a feature of this study was the use of undergraduate paraprofessionals trained in FFT who achieved equivalent outcomes in relation to recidivism as the senior graduate level therapists in earlier studies. Gordon (1995) went further and evaluated the impact on rates of reoffending of using paraprofessionals hired by the court with no graduate-level training in mental health services. Unlike previous studies, treatment for families of 17-18 year old chronic offenders was given in the home. Again, compared to regular services, the juveniles receiving FFT had a reduced rate of reconviction at the 18-month follow up.

Stemming from FFT, Gordon (2000) has developed an interactive CD-ROM based intervention called *Parenting Wisely* for use with families of at-risk children. The CD-ROM method was designed to overcome literacy barriers and meet the needs of parents who would not usually attend parenting education. *Parenting Wisely* requires limited agency resources and is designed to be used by parents who are unfamiliar with computers. A trial by Gordon and Kacir (1997) suggests promising outcomes for this approach. Eighty court-mandated parents of teenage offenders were either assigned by to take part in *Parenting Wisely* or to a 'usual treatment' control group (the young people were mostly given probation orders). Outcomes for the children in the intervention group included a decline in problem behaviour at one, three and six month's post-treatment compared to the control group. Parents in this group, mostly made up of single mothers, showed an increase in parenting knowledge compared to their control group peers (Gordon, 2000). This programme is being used by a few Youth Offending Teams in England with parents of young offenders subject to parenting orders (Ghate & Ramella, 2002). It has also been evaluated in Ireland using a small-scale randomised trial with promising results (O'Neill & Woodward, 2002).

Types of evaluation

Evaluations of FFT have included well-controlled investigations with random assignment to treatment conditions and with matched, but not randomly assigned, comparison groups. Some studies have also compared outcomes for families undertaking FFT with base rates for that population (Alexander et al, 1998). Most of the evaluations have occurred in

America with many of them conducted in Utah by the developers - although one study in Lund, Sweden of 95 young men arrested for serious offences found lower recidivism rates after two years among those who participated in FFT (50%) compared with a 'treatment as usual group' (80%) (Hansson, 1998). Most studies have included follow-up periods ranging from one to three years (most lasting more than a year), although one exception involved a five-year follow-up period examining the arrest rate for adults who had received FFT as adolescents (Gordon et al, 1995). The recidivism rate for the group that had received FFT was 9% compared to 41% of the control group.

The evaluators

The programme developers have conducted a number of evaluations. There have also been independent evaluations with consistent findings.

Settings

FFT has been successfully implemented cross-culturally and internationally, in urban and rural settings, and in a range of treatment settings including by independent providers, clinics, home-based programmes, and juvenile courts (Alexander et al, 1998).

Outcomes

The American evidence suggests that FFT can reduce adolescent re-arrests, reduce recidivism for a wide range of juvenile offences and significantly reduce potential new offending for the siblings of treated adolescents. There is also evidence of FFT's long-term effectiveness and positive post-intervention outcomes when delivered by paraprofessionals (Barton et al, 1985; Gordon et al, 1995).

Key messages concerning effectiveness

- FFT shows potential as an intervention for reducing recidivism in high-risk young people in the short and longer term – and also their siblings.

- FFT has achieved positive outcomes when delivered in a clinical or home setting, and when implemented by professionals or paraprofessionals.

7 Conclusions

This selective review of promising interventions for children at high risk of developing antisocial personality disorder (ASPD) has focused on six well-evidenced programmes: two parenting programmes, *The Incredible Years* (also known as the 'Webster-Stratton' programme) and *Triple P*; the *Nurse-Family Partnership* home visiting programme and three programmes for families and carers of high-need adolescents: *Multisystemic Therapy* (MST); *Multidimensional Treatment Foster Care* (MTFC); and *Functional Family Therapy* (FFT). All of these were developed and have mostly been implemented and evaluated overseas – *Triple P* in Australia, and the others in the United States. They are, however, in limited but growing use in the UK. Given the evidence available, recent British Government interest in these programmes (Social Exclusion Task Force, 2006) can be strongly endorsed.

Some of the programmes or their forerunners have been in development and use for many years (*Incredible Years, Nurse-Family Partnership, FFT*); others (like *Triple P*) are relative newcomers. They span a range of preventive tiers from universal ('primary') support services to targeted ('secondary' and 'tertiary') interventions. While some also operate in clinical settings, they have all been found to work in the homes and communities of young people and their families. Collectively, they can be said to form a suite of highly promising interventions ranged across the spectrum from early prevention intervention to later crisis and therapeutic responses.

Effectiveness

One immediate conclusion from this review is that the six programmes are supported by considerable evidence of their effectiveness in achieving better outcomes for children and young people; especially those whose early-onset behavioural problems place them at risk for 'life-course persistent' criminal involvement, antisocial behaviour and social exclusion. All have demonstrated effectiveness in the short to medium-term, and some have been evaluated over much longer periods. Although it has sometimes been possible to cite studies or reviews that raise pertinent questions about a programme's efficacy (notably their effectiveness under imperfect conditions), the main thrust of the scientific literature on these programmes is that they 'work'. While specific aspects of effectiveness vary between programmes, they have collectively been shown to reduce behaviour problems, including child and adolescent conduct disorders, which are the diagnostic precursors of adult antisocial personality disorder (ASPD). They are effective in reducing antisocial behaviour measured using young people's own reports and using official records. They have led to reductions in major risk factors, such as poor parental supervision and discipline, aggressive school behaviour and association with delinquent peers, and exposure to key protective factors such as social bonding and contact with adults setting healthy standards of behaviour. In addition, a number have directly demonstrated their capacity to reduce re-offending and reconviction rates for young offenders, including – in the case of MST (see below) – adult recidivism.

The evaluations of *Nurse-Family Partnership* (Olds et al, 1997) – an intervention implemented during pregnancy and the first two years of a child's life – provide an especially impressive testament to the potentially durable power of very early intervention. They also demonstrate the potential value to policy makers of sustained investment in rigorous, longitudinal evaluation of preventive initiatives. At the other end of the treatment age-range considered in this review, *Multisystemic Therapy* (MST) for chronic juvenile offenders and their families has yielded positive effects on repeat offending (relative to a 'conventional' course of individual therapy) stretching well into their young adult lives (Schaeffer & Borduin, 2005).

Some of the programmes also show evidence of cost-effectiveness, in that the costs of treatment are outweighed substantially by the savings to the public purse when later poor outcomes are averted or moderated or when compared to 'usual' treatment methods. All programmes also show evidence of benefits for parents (reduced parenting problems, improved mental health), and some also show positive results for wider family, including siblings of the 'treated' child. All programmes also show evidence of benefits across different cultural and ethnic groups, to the extent that this has been trialled and evaluated.

Key features of effective programmes

It is clear from the large literature on 'what works' in reducing offending (and a range of other social intervention fields) that implementation matters critically. Content is important, but equally important is the way in which the intervention is delivered on the ground. Without good implementation, the best-planned interventions will fail.

The six featured programmes are especially illuminating as they share a number of general principles of effective implementation (and therefore, of effectiveness *per se*). These are outlined below. It is also worth emphasising that in the few studies where these programmes were not found to be effective, there were almost always questions about the quality of implementation.

- All the programmes have a **strong, coherent and clearly articulated theoretical basis**. Content is driven by what is currently known about how families function, what is optimal for children's development, what are the key risk and protective factors for negative behaviours in children and youth, and how to interrupt negative cycles of child and family behaviour.

- All the six programmes use **professional, qualified and/or trained staff** to deliver the work with families. Training consists of a background in one of a range of professional social care disciplines (e.g social work, child and adolescent mental health, youth justice, nursing, primary health care) plus specific training, often accompanied by formal accreditation, in delivering the programme. The possible exceptions are the *Nurse-Family Partnership* programme and FFT, which can use paraprofessionals (for example pre-qualified undergraduate level students); but even in this case the workers are specially trained and closely supervised. It should be noted, however, that a comparative evaluation of the *Nurse Family Partnership* found smaller, positive, effects on child development achieved by paraprofessionals than by qualified nurses (Olds et al., 2004b)

- All the interventions have **high 'programme fidelity'**. They are delivered according to a thoroughly documented 'curriculum', which is carefully monitored to ensure the staff stay faithful to the principles and the prescribed methods of the intervention.

- All the programmes are delivered **in the natural environments of families and young people** – i.e. in homes, and in local community settings. Though some element of clinic-based treatment may be involved, 'in situ' work predominates, meaning that workers can help families tackle directly the real life challenges they face. However, all the programmes are also **tailored to the needs of their core clientele**, whether they are parents of young children beginning to exhibit the first clear signs of behaviour problems, or families and young people in chronically stressed, high need circumstances. They all aim for flexibility to respond to individual needs but without loss of fidelity to the core programme and its key principles.

- The programmes have **partnership with families** as a core principle. The driving ethos is for collaborative working, respecting parents and young people as experts in their own lives, and empowering them to seek solutions to their own problems wherever possible.

- All the programmes are **multi-modal** or **multi-dimensional**. This means they all incorporate a number of different methods of working with families, so that different preferences and learning styles can be accommodated, and different problems can be tackled simultaneously. All of the programmes work directly with parents or carers. Methods range from supported self-directed learning to videotape modelling to group work to intensive individual one-to-one counselling and therapy. They may also use drug treatment and formal psychiatric treatment where indicated. Some programmes also include work with children, young people and other family members; or – in the case of *The Incredible Years* – offer a separate module that complements their work with parents. However, work with young people at high risk of offending requires care to avoid the creation of negative peer groups that can contribute to worse outcomes (Dishion & Andrews, 1995; Dishion et al, 1999).

- A **tiered approach** is built into some of the programmes, so that support can be 'ratcheted up' to the next level or extended to more people in the family if initial intervention is not having the desired effect. *Triple P* adopts this approach most overtly, having five levels of intervention, but other programmes also allow for a graduated approach.

- **None of these programmes is a 'quick fix'**. All offer a relatively sustained treatment period and a high degree of face-to-face work with parents and children. The initial input is thus relatively sustained to achieve the longer term payoff.

Other issues, and what is still unknown

Some caveats remain, despite this mainly positive picture:

The first is that because all the programmes were developed outside Britain, uncertainty remains about how well some of the programmes would translate to the UK. However, *The Incredible Years* has been rigorously evaluated in the UK, with very promising results and current government interest in piloting other programmes, including *Triple P*, *Nurse-Family Partnership* and *Multisystemic Therapy*, is encouraging. The value of evaluating such trials using research designs at least as robust as those used in other countries to establish their effectiveness should be self-evident.

Although outcomes from *Nurse-Family Partnership* (15 years) and *Multisystemic Therapy* (14 years) have, exceptionally, been followed-up over many years, there is a general shortage of information concerning the longer-term, sustainable effects of prevention programmes. In some cases, including evaluations of *The Incredible Years*, the choice on ethical grounds of 'waiting list' comparison groups, means that controlled measurements of long-term outcomes are, by definition, impossible. Effectiveness in reducing child and adolescent conduct disorders can be read as highly promising evidence in the right direction. But, with the exception of MST, the evidence concerning the relevance of these programmes as a means of reducing ASPD does not yet extend into adulthood.

Third, although by the standards of public health interventions in general these top-of-the-range programmes report an enviable success rate, they also experience **a considerable degree of treatment failure**, either due to families dropping out midway through the programme or because of failure to engage at the outset. Non-engagement and premature drop-out rates are typically lower for these programmes than other, less rigorously implemented family and child support services, where a failure rate of around one third of cases is not uncommon. Nevertheless, it should be acknowledged that even the most effective and evidenced programmes do not work for all people under all conditions. Knowledge about what predicts treatment failure – **what does not work and why** – is still sketchy. Many evaluation studies do not provide a full picture (often for valid reasons such as lack of data, though the substantial involvement of programme originators in much of the research may not help to focus attention on the failures as well as successes of interventions). What little evidence exists suggests that within a 'treated' population it is generally the most needy, most challenging families and young people who are least helped by these programmes. In families where parents have mental health problems, where there is substance misuse, or where there is a background of serious abuse and neglect the outcomes are often least positive. Further research is needed to distil the key factors that predict treatment failure.

Finally, the importance of **careful targeting** and of **refining the tools available for early risk assessment** continue to press. These are sensitive issues: not least in relation to children at the start of their lives whose exposure to risk, no matter how great, cannot justify stigmatising them as the anti-social adults of the future. As Sutton and colleagues (2004) insist, the way to make interventions acceptable is to stress their relevance to children's future health and happiness while reducing the immediate problems facing parents. Even when young people have passed the age of criminal responsibility, and offending can result in court-ordered intervention for their families, there is evidence that a supportive, non-blaming approach can help gain a degree of acceptance among parents (Ghate & Ramella, 2002). It is also clear that most of the programmes described in this review require careful targeting as an inevitable consequence of their intensity and cost. Most recently, the case for targeting children with diagnosable problems has been made in relation to *The Incredible Years*, after Scott and colleagues (2006) found few measurable behaviour difficulties among children in a disadvantaged neighbourhood where the programme was made universally available.

However, the practice of targeting children and families is complicated. Although individual programmes may have their own assessment and referral instruments, the lack of a common standard for identifying need and referring children and families to support services means that the potential for early intervention is constrained. For example, one study in the mid-1990s found no fewer than 77 different guidelines in use among English and Welsh Health Visitors to identify vulnerable families in need of extra support. Most of these were judged to be "subjective and invalid in nature" (Appleton, 1997). At the moment, we simply cannot be sure whether all the families and children who may benefit from intervention are being appropriately referred. The Common Assessment Framework recently introduced in England for use by professionals working with children and young people aged 0 to 18 seeks to provide a shared method for identifying 'additional needs' (including disruptive and antisocial behaviour) and 'complex needs' (including significant mental health problems and involvement with the youth justice system). But even this attempt to achieve greater consistency comes without a formal scoring system. Scope exists, however, to develop and a scoring system for children at risk of conduct disorders and ASPD as a further 'filter' once children's additional or complex needs have been determined. Early Assessment of Risk Lists (EARLs) devised, separately, for boys and girls in Canada as a way of assessing individual risks of offending offer one route that merits further investigation (Augimeri et al, 2001; Levene et al, 2001).

The task of developing robust instruments is fraught with difficulties; not least those associated with the important issue of 'false positives' and stigmatising children with labels that unintentionally damage their life chances. But the existence of high-risk children whose needs are overlooked until they begin to manifest clear and serious difficulties is also a significant problem for society. Although later intervention is better than no intervention at all, research provides us with ample evidence that if we wait until problems are severe and entrenched, then we have waited too long.

Bibliography

Alexander, J. F. & Parsons, B. V. (1973) Short-term behavioural intervention with delinquent families: Impact on family process and recidivism. *Journal of Abnormal Psychology*, 81, pp.219-225.

Alexander, J., Pugh, C., Parsons, B. & Sexton, T. (1998) *Blueprints for Violence Prevention: Functional Family Therapy*. Colorado, U.S.: Center for the Study and Prevention of Violence.

American Psychiatric Association (1994) *Diagnostic and statistical manual of mental disorders* (4th edition). Washington D.C.: American Psychiatric Association.

Anderson, B., Beinart, S., Farrington, D., Longman, J., Sturgis, P. & Utting, D. (2001) *Risk and Protective Factors Associated with Youth Crime and Effective Interventions to Prevent It*. London: Youth Justice Board.

Aos, S., Lieb, R., Mayfield, J., Miller, M. & Pennucci, A. (2004) *Benefits and Costs of Prevention and Early Intervention Programs for Youth*. Olympia: Washington State Institute for Public Policy.

Appleton, J. V. (1997) Establishing the validity and reliability of clinical practice guidelines used to identify families requiring health visitor support. *Public Health*, 111, pp 107-113.

Augimeri, L., Koegl, C., Webster, C. D., & Levene, K. (2001) *The Early Assessment of Risk List for Boys (EARL-20B), Version 2*. Toronto: Child Development Institute.

Bandura, A. (ed.) (1995) *Self-efficacy in changing societies*. Cambridge: Cambridge University Press.

Bank, L., Patterson, G. R. & Reid, J. B. (1987) Delinquency prevention through training parents in family management. *Journal of Applied Behavior Analysis*, 10, pp.75-82.

Barker, W. (1994) *Child Protection: the impact of the Child Development Programme*. Bristol: Early Childhood Development Centre.

Barker, W. & Anderson, R. (1988) *The Child Development Programme: an Evaluation of Process and Outcomes (Evaluation Document 9.)* Bristol: Early Childhood Development Centre.

Barker W. & Anderson, R. (1989) Response to Critique of the CDP's Evaluation Document 9. *The Psychologist*, 11, pp.483-485.

Barkley, R. A. et al (2000) Multi-method psycho-educational intervention for preschool children with disruptive behaviour: preliminary results at post-treatment. *Journal of Child Psychology and Psychiatry*, 41, pp.319-332

Barlow, A. *et al* (2006) Home-visiting intervention to improve child care among American Indian adolescent mothers. *Archives of Pediatrics and Adolescent Medicine*, 160 (11) pp.1101-1107.

Barlow, J. (1999) 'What works in parent education programmes', in Lloyd, E. (ed.) *Parenting Matters: What Works in Parenting Education?* pp.64-84. Barkingside: Barnardos.

Barnes, J. and Freude-Lagevardi, A. (2003) *From Pregnancy to Early Childhood: Early Interventions to Enhance the Mental Health of Childen and Families. Vol. 1 Report.* London: The Mental Health Foundation.

Barton, C., Alexander, J. F., Waldron, H., Turner, C. W. (1985) Generalizing treatment effects of Functional Family Therapy: Three replications. *American Journal of Family Therapy*, 13, pp.16-26.

Bauman, K. E., Ennett, S. T., Foshee, V. A., Pemberton, M., King, T. S. & Koch, G. G. (2002) Influence of a Family Program on Adolescent Smoking and Drinking Prevalence. *Prevention Science*, 3, pp.35–42.

Beinart, S., Anderson, B., Lee, S. & Utting, D. (2002) *Youth at Risk? A National Survey of Risk Factors, Protective Factors and Problem Behaviour among Young People in England, Scotland and Wales.* London. Communities that Care.

Bhabra, S., Dinos, S. and Ghate, D. (2006a) *Young People, Risk, and Protection: A Major Survey of Primary Schools in On Track Areas.* London: Department for Education and Skills.

Bhabra, S., Dinos, S. and Ghate, D. (2006b) *Young People, Risk, and Protection: A Major Survey of Secondary Schools in On Track Areas.* London: Department for Education and Skills.

Bilukha, O., Hahn, R. A., Crosby, A., Fullilove, M. T., Liberman, A., Moscicki, E., Snyder, S., Tuma, F., Corso, P., Schofield, A., & Briss, P. A. (2005) The Effectiveness of Early Childhood Home Visitation in Preventing Violence: A Systematic Review. *American Journal of Preventive Medicine*, 28, pp.11-39.

Botvin, G. J., Baker, E., Dusenbury, L., Botvin, E. M. & Diaz, T. (1995) Long-term follow-up results of a randomized drug abuse prevention trial in a white middle-class population. *Journal of the American Medical Association*, 273, pp.1106-1112.

Bourdin, C. M., Mann, B. J., Cone, L. T., Henggeler, S. W., Fucci, B. R., Blaske, D. M. & Williams, R. A. (1995) Multisystemic treatment of serious juvenile offenders: Long-term prevention of criminality and violence. *Journal of Consulting and Clinical Psychology*, 63, pp.569-578.

Borduin, C. M. & Schaeffer, C. M. (2001) Multisystemic treatment of juvenile sexual offenders: A progress report. *Journal of Psychology and Human Sexuality*, 13, pp.25-42.

Brewer, D. D., Hawkins, J. D., Catalano, R. F. & Neckerman, H. J. (1995) 'Preventing Serious, Violent and Chronic Juvenile Offending. A Review of Evaluations of Selected Strategies in Childhood, Adolescence and the Community', in Howell, J. C., Krisberg, B., Hawkins, J. D. & Wilson, J. J. (eds.) *A Sourcebook: Serious, Violent & Chronic Juvenile Offenders.* London: Sage.

Brook, J. S., Brook, D. W., Gordon, A. S., Whiteman, M. & Cohen, P. (1990) 'The psychosocial etiology of adolescent drug use: A family interactional approach'. *General, Social and General Psychology Monographs*, 116 (Whole No 2).

Brosnan, R. & Carr, A. (2000) 'Adolescent conduct problems', in Carr, A. (ed.) *What Works with Children and Adolescents?: A critical review of psychological interventions with children, adolescents and their families.* pp.131-154. (Florence, KY, US.: Taylor and Francis/Routledge).

Brunk, M., Henggeler, S. W. & Whelan, J. P. (1987) Comparison of multisystemic therapy and parent training in the brief treatment of child abuse and neglect. *Journal of Consulting Clinical Psychology*, 55, pp.171-178

Bynner, J. (1999) *Risks and Outcomes of Social Exclusion. Insights from Longitudinal Data. Report for the Organization for Economic Cooperation and Development (OECD).* London: Institute of Education.

Catalano, R. F. & Hawkins, J. D. (1996) 'The Social Development Model: A Theory of Antisocial Behavior', in Hawkins, J. D. (ed.) *Delinquency and Crime. Current Theories.* Cambridge: Cambridge University Press.

Chamberlain P. (1990) Comparative evaluation of specialized foster care for seriously delinquent youths: A first step. *Community Alternatives: International Journal of Family Care*, 2 (2), pp.21-36.

Chamberlain, P. (1998) *Blueprints for Violence Prevention: Multidimensional Treatment Foster Care.* Colorado, U.S: Institute of Behavioral Science.

Chamberlain, P., Moreland, S. & Reid, K. (1992) Enhanced services and stipends for foster parents: effects on retention rates and outcomes for children. *Child Welfare League of America*, LXXI, pp.387-401.

Chamberlain, P. & Reid, J. B. (1991) Using a specialized foster care community treatment model for children and adolescents leaving the state mental hospital. *Journal of Community Psychology*, 19, pp.266-276.

Chamberlain, P. & Reid, J. B. (1998) Comparison of two community alternatives to incarceration for chronic juvenile offenders. *Journal of Consulting and Clinical Psychology*, 66 (4), pp.624-633.

Christensen, A. P. & Sanders, M. R. (1987) Habit reversal and differential reinforcement of other behaviour in the treatment of thumb-sucking: an analysis of generalization and side effects. *Journal of Child Psychology and Psychiatry*, 28 (2), pp.281-295.

Coie, J. D., Watt, N. F., West, S. G., Hawkins, J. D., Asarnow, H. J., Markman, H. J., Ramey, S. L., Shure, M. & Long, B. (1993) The Science of Prevention: A Conceptual Framework and Some Directions for a National Research Program. *American Psychologist*, 48, pp.1012-1022.

Conduct Problems Prevention Group (1999) Initial impact of Fast Track prevention trial for conduct problems: I: The High-Risk Sample. *Journal of Consulting and Clinical Psychology*, 67, pp.631-47.

Conduct Problems Prevention Research Group (2002) Evaluation of the first three years of the Fast Track prevention trail with children at high risk for adolescent conduct problems. *Journal of Abnormal Child Psychology, 30,* pp19-35.

Conduct Problems Prevention Research Group (2006) *Fast Track Project Overview.* Available on-line: http://www.pubpol.duke.edu/centers /child/fasttrack/fasttrackoverview.htm accessed 10.01.07

Conger, R. D., Patterson, G. R. & Ge, X. (1995) It takes two to replicate: A mediational model for the impact of parents' stress on adolescent adjustment. *Child Development, 66,* pp.80-97.

Connell, S., Sanders, M. R., & Markie-Dadds, C. (1997) Self-directed behavioural family intervention for parents of oppositional children in rural and remote areas. *Behaviour Modification, 21* (4), pp.379-408.

Cullen, K. J. (1976) A six-year controlled trial of prevention of children's behaviour disorders. *Journal of Paediatrics, 88,* pp.662-666.

Cunningham, C. E., Bremner, R. & Boyle, M. (1995) Large group community-based parenting programmes for families of pre-schoolers at risk from disruptive disorders: Utilisation, cost-effectiveness and outcome. *Journal of Child Psychology and Psychiatry and Allied Disciplines,* Vol. 36, pp.1141-1159.

Curtis, N. M., Ronan, K. R. & Borduin, C. M. (2004) Multisystemic treatment: A meta-analysis of outcome studies. *American Psychological Association, 18* (3), pp.411-419.

Davis, H., Spurr, P., Cox, A., Lynch, M., von Roenne, A. & Hahn, K. (1997) A description and evaluation of a community child mental health service. *Clinical Child Psychology and Psychiatry, 2,* pp.221-238.

Davis, H. & Spurr, P. (1998) Parent Counselling: An Evaluation of a Community Child Mental Health Service. *Journal of Child Psychology and Psychiatry, 39* (3), pp.365-376.

Devilly, G. J. & Sanders, M. R. (1993) 'Hey Dad, Watch me': the effects of training a child to teach pain management skills to a parent with recurrent headaches. *Behaviour Change, 10* (4), pp.237-243.

DfES (2003) *Every Child Matters* Cm 5860. London: The Stationery Office.

Dishion, T. J. & Andrews, D. W. (1995) Preventing escalation in problem behaviors with high-risk young adolescents: immediate and 1-year outcomes. *Journal of Consulting and Clinical Psychology, 63,* pp.538-48.

Dishion T. J, McCord, J. and Poulin, F. (1999) When interventions harm: peer groups and problem behaviour *American Psychologist* 54 (9) pp.755-764.

Dishion, T. J. & Andrews, D. W. (1995) Preventing escalation in problem behaviors with high-risk young adolescents: immediate and 1-year outcomes. *Journal of Consulting and Clinical Psychology, 63,* pp.538-48.

Dishion T. J., McCord, J. & Poulin, F. (1999) When interventions harm: peer groups and problem behaviour. *American Psychologist* 54 (9) pp.755-764.

Dodge, K. A. & Schwartz, D. (1997) 'Social information processing mechanisms in aggressive behavior', in Stoff, D., Breiling, J. & Maser, J. D. (eds.) *Handbook of antisocial behavior*. Chichester: Wiley.

Eckenrode, J., Zielinski, D., Smith, E., Marcynyszyn, L. A., Henderson, C. R., Kitzman, H., Cole, R., Powers, J., & Olds, D. L. (2001) Child maltreatment and the early onset of problem behaviors: Can a program of nurse home visitation break the link? *Development and Psychopathology*, 13, pp.873-890.

Eddy, Bridges-Whaley, R. & Chamberlain, P. (2004) The prevention of violent behavior by chronic and serious male juvenile offenders: A 2-year follow-up of a randomized clinical trial. *Journal of Emotional and Behavioral Disorders*, 12 (1), pp.2-8.

Egeland, B., Carlson, E. & Sroufe, L. A. (1993) Resilience as process. *Development and Psychopathology*, 5, pp.517-528.

Elkan, R., Kendrick, D., Hewitt, M., Robinson, J. J. A., Tolley, K , Blair, M et al (2000) The effectiveness of domiciliary health visiting: a systematic review of international studies and a selective review of the British literature. *Health Technology Assessment*, 4 (13).

Ellis, D. A., Frey, M. A., Naar-King, S., Templin, T., Cunningham, P. B. & Cakan, N. (2005) Use of multisystemic therapy to improve regimen adherence among adolescents with type 1 diabetes in chronic poor metabolic control: A randomized controlled trial. *Diabetes Care*, 28, pp.1604-1610.

Emond, A., Pollock, J., Deave, T., Bonnell, S., Peters, T. J. & Harvey, I. (2002) An evaluation of the First Parent Health Visitor Scheme. *Archives of Disease in Childhood*, 86, pp.150-157.

Farrington, D. P. (1991) Antisocial personality from childhood to adulthood. *The Psychologist*, 4, pp.389-394.

Farrington, D. P. (1993) 'Understanding and preventing bullying', in Tonry, M. & Morris, N. (eds.) *Crime and Justice Vol. 17*. Chicago: University of Chicago Press.

Farrington, D. P. (1996) *Understanding and Preventing Youth Crime*. York: Joseph Rowntree Foundation / York Publishing Services

Farrington, D. P. (2000) Explaining and preventing crime: the globalization of knowledge. *Criminology*, 38, pp.801-824.

Farrington, D. P. (2003) 'Advancing knowledge about the early prevention of adult antisocial behaviour', in Farrington, D. P. & Coid, J. W. (eds.) *Early Prevention of Adult Antisocial Behaviour*. Cambridge: Cambridge University Press.

Farrington, D. P. (2004) 'Conduct disorder, aggression and delinquency', in Lerner R. M. & Steinberg L. (eds.) *Handbook of Adolescent Psychology (2nd edition)*. New York: Wiley.

Farrington, D. P. (2007) 'Childhood Risk Factors and Risk-focused Prevention', in Maguire, M., Morgan, R., & Reiner, R. (eds.) *The Oxford Handbook of Criminology* (4th edition). Oxford: Oxford University Press.

Farrington, D. P. & Welsh, B. C. (2003) Family-based Prevention of Offending: A Meta-analysis. *The Australian and New Zealand Journal of Criminology*. 36, pp.127-151.

Farrington, D. P. & West, D. J. (1993) Criminal, penal and life histories of chronic offenders: Risk and protective factors and early identification. *Criminal Behaviour and Mental Health*, 3, pp.492-523.

Fisher, P. A. & Chamberlain, P. (2000) Multidimensional treatment foster care: A program for intensive parenting, family support, and skill building *Journal of Emotional and Behavioral Disorders*, 8, pp.155-164.

Fisher, P. A., Gunnar, M. R., Chamberlain, P. & Reid, J. B. (2000) Preventive intervention for maltreated preschool children: Impact on children's behavior, neuroendocrine activity, and foster parent functioning. *Journal of the American Academy of Child and Adolescent Psychiatry*, 39, (11) pp.1356-1364.

France, A. & Utting D. (2005) The Paradigm of 'Risk and Protection-Focused Prevention' and its Impact on Services for Children and Families. *Children & Society*, 19 (2) pp.77-90

Gardner, F., Hutchings, J. & Lane, E. (2004) 'Three to eight years: risk and protective factors; effective interventions' in Sutton C., Utting D., & Farrington D.P.(eds.) *Support from the Start*. Nottingham: DfES.

Gardner, F., Burton, J. & Klimes, I. (2006) Randomised controlled trial of a parenting intervention in the voluntary sector for reducing child conduct problems: outcomes and mechanisms for change. *Journal of Child Psychology and Psychiatry and Allied Disciplines*, 47 (11), pp.1123-1132.

Garmezy, N. (1985) Stress-resistant children: The search for protective factors in Stevenson, J. E. (ed.) *Recent research in developmental psychopathology* (pp.213-233). New York: Elsevier Science.

Garmezy, N. (1993) 'Developmental Psychopathology: Some Historical and Current Perspectives', in Magnusson, D. & Caesar, P. (eds.) *Longitudinal Research on Individual Development*. Cambridge: Cambridge University Press.

Ghate, D. & Ramella, M. (2002) *Positive Parenting: the national evaluation of the Youth Justice Board's Parenting Programme*. London: Youth Justice Board.

Gomby, D .S., Larson, C. S., Lewitt, M. E. & Behrman, R. E. (1993) Home visiting: Analysis and Recommendations. *The Future of Children*, 3 (3), pp.6-22.

Gomby, D. S., Culross, P. L. & Behrman, R. E. (1999) Home Visiting: Recent Program Evaluations Analysis and Recommendations. *The Future of Children* 9 (1), pp.4-26.

Gordon, D. A. (1995) Functional family therapy for delinquents, in Ross, R. R., Antonowicz, D.H. & Dhaliwal, G.K. (eds.) *Going Straight: Effective Delinquency Prevention and Offender Rehabilitation* (pp.163-178) (Ottawa, Canada: Air training and Publications.

Gordon, D. A. (2000) Parent training via CD-ROM: Using technology to disseminate effective prevention practices. *Journal of Primary prevention*, 21 (2) pp.227-251.

Gordon, D. A., Graves, K. & Arbuthnot, J. (1995) The effect of functional family therapy for delinquents on adult criminal behavior. *Criminal Justice and Behavior*, 22 (1), pp.60-73.

Gordon, D. A. & Kacir, C. (1997) *Effectiveness of an interactive parent training program for changing adolescent behavior for court-referred parents.* Unpublished manuscript cited on www.familyworksinc.com/research_articles/index.html 09/01/2007

Gorsuch, R. L., Butler, M. C. (1976) Initial drug abuse: a review of predisposing social psychological factors. *Psychol Bull* 83(1) pp 120-137.

Greenberg, M. T., Kusche, C. A., Cook, E. T., & Quamma, J. P. (1995) Promoting emotional competence in school-aged children: The effects of the PATHS Curriculum. *Development and Psychopathology*, 7, pp.117-136.

Greenberg, M., Kusche, C. & Mihalic, S. (1998) *Promoting Alternative Thinking Strategies*, in Elliot, D. S. (Series ed.), *Blueprints for Violence Prevention, Book 10*. Colorado, US: Center for the Study and Prevention of Violence, Institute of Behavioral Science, University of Colorado.

Gross, D., Fogg, L., Webster-Stratton, C., Garvey, C., Julion, W. & Grady, J. (2003) Parent training with families of toddlers in day care in low-income urban communities. *Journal of Consulting & Clinical Psychology*, 7, *pp.261-278.*

Hansson, K. (1998) Functional family therapy replication in Sweden: Treatment outcome with juvenile delinquents. Paper presented to the Eighth International Conference on treating addictive behaviours. Santa Fe, New Mexico, February 1998. As cited in Alexander, J., Pugh, C., Parsons, B. & Sexton, T. (1998) *Blueprints for Violence Prevention: Functional Family Therapy*. Colorado U.S.: Center for the Study and Prevention of Violence.

Hardiker, P., Exton, K. & Barker, M. (1991) *Policies and Practices in Preventive Child Care*. (Avebury/Gower).

Hawkins, J. D., Catalano, R. F. & Miller, J. Y. (1992) Risk and Protective Factors for Alcohol and Other Drug Problems in Adolescence and Early Adulthood: Implications for Substance Abuse Prevention. *Psychological Bulletin*, 112 (1), pp.64-105.

Hawkins, J. D., Catalano, R. F. & Brewer, D. D. (1995) 'Preventing Serious, Violent and Chronic Juvenile Offending. Effective Strategies in Childhood, Adolescence and the Community,' in Howell, J. C., Krisberg, B., Hawkins, J. D. & Wilson, J. J. (eds.) *A Sourcebook: Serious, Violent & Chronic Juvenile Offenders*. London: Sage.

Hawkins, J. D., Herrenkohl, T., Farrington, D. P., Brewer, D., Catalano, R. F. & Harachi, T. W. (1998) 'A Review of Predictors of Youth Violence', in Farrington, D. P. & Loeber, R. (eds.) *Serious and Violent Juvenile Offenders: Risk Factors and Successful Interventions*. London: Sage.

Hawkins, J. D., Smith, B. H., Hill, K. G., Kosterman, R., Catalano, R. F. & Abbot, R. D. (2003) 'Understanding and Preventing Crime and Violence: Findings from the Seattle Social Development Project' in Thornberry, T. P. & Krohn, M. D., (eds.) *Taking Stock of Delinquency: An Overview of Findings from Contemporary Longitudinal Studies*. New York: Kluwer/Plenum.

Henggeler, S. W. (1997) Treating Serious Anti-Social Behavior in Youth: The MST Approach, *Juvenile Justice Bulletin* May 1997. Washington D.C.: OJJDP.

Henggeler, S. W., Melton, G. & Smith, L. A. (1992) Family preservation using multisystemic therapy: An effective alternative to incarcerating serious juvenile offenders. *Journal of Consulting and Clinical Psychology*, 60 (6), pp.953-961.

Henggeler, S. W. (1998) *Blueprints for Violence Prevention: Multisystemic Therapy*. Colorado US: Centre for the Study and Prevention of Violence.

Henggeler, S. W., Melton, G., Brondino, M. J. & Scherer, D. G. (1997) Multisystemic therapy with violent and chronic juvenile offenders and their families: The role of treatment fidelity in successful dissemination. *Journal of Consulting and Clinical Psychology*, 65 (5) pp.821-833.

Henggeler, S. W., Schoenwald, S. K., Borduin, C. M., Rowland, M. D. & Cunningham, P. B. (1998) *Multisystemic Treatment of Antisocial Behavior in Children and Adolescents* New York: The Guilford Press.

Henggeler, S. W., Schoenwald, S. K. & Pickrel, S. G. (1995) Multisystemic therapy: Bridging the gap between university –and community-based treatment. *Journal of Consulting and Clinical Psychology*, 63 (5), pp.709-717.

Henggeler, S. W., Clingempeel, G. W., Brondino, M. J. & Pickrel, S. G. (2002) Four-year follow-up of multisystemic therapy with substance-abusing and substance-dependent juvenile offenders. *Journal American Academy of Child and Adolescent Psychiatry*, 41 (7), pp.868-874.

Henry, B., Caspi, A., Moffitt, T. E. & Sylva, P. A. (1996) Temperamental and familial predictors of violent and non-violent criminal convictions: age 3 to age 18. *Developmental Psychology*, 32, pp.614-623

Hetherington, E. M., Cox, M. & Cox, R. (1982) Effects of divorce on parents and children, in Lamb, M. (ed.) *Non-traditional families*. Hillsdale NJ: Erlbaum.

Hoath, F. E. & Sanders, M.R. (2002) A feasibility study of enhanced Triple P positive parenting program for parents of children with attention deficit hyperactivity disorder. *Behaviour Change*, 19 (4), pp.191-206.

Hodnett, E.D. & Roberts, I. (2000) *Home-based Social Support for Socially Disadvantaged Mothers. The Cochrane Library, Issue 3*. Oxford: Update Software.

Huey, S. J., Henggeler, S. W., Rowland, M. D., Halliday-Boykins, C. A., Cunningham, P. B., Pickrel, S. G. & Edwards, J. (2004) Multisystemic therapy effects on attempted suicide by youths presenting psychiatric emergencies. *J Am Acad Child Adolesc Psychiatry*, 43 (2) pp.183-190.

Hutchings, J., Bywater, T., Davies, C. & Whitaker, C. (2006) Do crime rates predict the outcome of parenting programmes for parents of 'high-risk' preschool children? *Educational & Child Psychology*, Vol 23 (2), pp.15-25.

Jenkins, J. M. & Smith, M. A. (1990) Factors protecting children living in disharmonious homes: Maternal reports: *Journal of the American Academy of Child and Adolescent Psychiatry*, 29, pp.60-69.

Jessor, R. & Jessor, S.L. (1977) Problem Behavior and Psychosocial Development: A longitudinal study of youth. New York: Academic Press.

Johnson, Z., Howell, F. & Molloy, B. (1993) Community mothers programme: randomized controlled trial of non-professional intervention in parenting. *British Medical Journal*, 306, pp.1449-1452.

Johnson, Z., Molloy, B., Scallan, E., Fitzpatrick, P., Rooney, B., Keegan, T. & Byrne, P. (2000) Community Mothers Programme – seven year follow-up of a randomized controlled trial of non-professional intervention in parenting. *Journal of Public Health Medicine*, 22, pp.337-342.

Karoly, L., Greenwood, P. W., Everingham, S. S., Hoube, J., Kilburn, M. R., Rydell, C. P., Sanders, M. & Chiesa, J. (1998) *Investing in Our Children: What We Know and Don't Know About the Costs and Benefits of Early Childhood Interventions*. Santa Monica, California: RAND Corporation.

Kazdin, A. E. (1997) Parent management training: Evidence, outcomes and issues, *Journal of the American Academy of Child and Adolescent Psychiatry*, 36, pp.1349-1356.

Kazdin, A.E. (2005) *Parent Management Training*. New York: Oxford University Press.

Kazdin, A. E., Siegel, T. C., & Bass, D. (1992) Cognitive problem-solving skills training and parent management training in the treatment of antisocial behaviour in children. *Journal of Consulting and Clinical Psychology*, 60, pp.733-47.

Kitzman, H., Olds D. L., Henderson, C. R., Hanks, C., Cole, R., Tatelbaum, R. et al. (1997) Effect of prenatal and infancy home visitation by nurses on pregnancy outcomes, childhood injuries and repeated childbearing: A randomized controlled trial. *Journal of the American Medical Association*, 278, pp.644-652.

Kitzman, H., Olds, D. L., Sidora, K., Henderson, C. R., Hanks, C., Cole, R., Luckey, D. W., Bondy, J., Cole, K. & Glazner, J. (2000) Enduring effects of nurse home visitation on maternal life course. *The Journal of the American Medical Association*, 283 (15) pp.1983-1989

Kempf, K. (1993) 'The empirical status of Hirschi's control theory', in Adler, F. & Laufer, W. S. (eds.) *New directions in criminological theory: Vol. 4. Advances in criminological theory*, New Brunswick, Canada: Transaction.

Klein, N. C., Alexander, J. F., and Parsons, B. V. (1977) Impact of family systems intervention on recidivism and sibling delinquency: A model of primary prevention and program evaluation. *Journal of Consulting and Clinical Psychology*, 45, pp.469-474.

Kolvin, I., Miller, F. J. W., Scott, D. M., Gatzanis, S. R. M. & Fleeting, M. (1990) *Continuities of Deprivation?* Aldershot: Avebury.

Korfmacher, J., O'Brien, R., Hiatt, S. & Olds, D. (1999) Differences in program implementation between nurses and paraprofessionals providing home visits during pregnancy and infancy: A randomized trial. *American Journal of Public Health*, 89 (12), pp.1847-1851.

Lane, E., Gardner, F., Hutchings, J. & Jacobs, B. (2004) 'Nine to Thirteen Years' in Sutton, C., Utting D. & Farrington D.P. (eds.) *Support from the Start*. Nottingham: DfES.

Larzelere, R. E. & Patterson, G. R. (1990) Parental Management: mediator of the effect of socioeconomic status on early delinquency. *Criminology*, 28 (2) pp.301-324.

Le Blanc, M. (1998) 'Screening of Serious and Violent Juvenile Offenders: Identification, Classification and Prediction', in Farrington, D. P. & Loeber, R. (eds.) *Serious and Violent Juvenile Offenders: Risk Factors and Successful Interventions*. London: Sage.

Leschied, A. W. & Cunningham, A. (2002) *Seeking effective interventions for young offenders: Interim results of a four-year randomised study of multisytemic therapy in Ontario, Canada*. London, Ontario, Canada: Centre for Children and Families in the Justice System.

Leve, L. D. & Chamberlain, P. (2005) Association with delinquent peers: intervention effects for youth in the juvenile justice system. *Journal of Abnormal Child Psychology*, 33 (3), pp.339-347.

Levene, K. S., Augimeri, L. K., Pepler, D. J., Walsh, M. M., Webster, C. D., & Koegl, C. J. (2001) *Early Assessment Risk List for Girls (EARL-21G), Version 1,* Consultation Edition. Toronto: Child Development Institute.

Littell, J. H., Popa, M. & Forsythe, B. (2005) Multisystematic therapy for social, emotional, and behavioral problems in youth aged 10-17. *The Cochrane Database of Systematic Reviews,* 2005, Issue 4.

Lipsey, M. W. & Derzon, J. H. (1998) 'Predictors of Violent or Serious Delinquency in Adolescence and Early Adulthood. A Synthesis of Longitudinal Research', in Loeber, R. & Farrington, D. P. (eds.) *Serious & Violent Juvenile Offenders: Risk Factors and Successful Interventions.* London: Sage.

Loeber, R. & Stouthamer-Loeber, M. (1986) 'Family factors as correlates and predictors of antisocial conduct problems and delinquency', in Morris, N. & Tonry, M. (eds.) *Crime and Justice, Vol. 7.* Chicago: University of Chicago Press.

Loeber, R. & Hay, D. F. (1996) Key issues in the development of aggression and violence from childhood to early adulthood. *Annual Review of Psychology,* 48, pp.371-410.

Loeber, R., Green, S. M. & Lahey, B. B. (2003) 'Risk factors for adult antisocial personality,' in Farrington, D. P. & Coid, J. W. (eds.) *Early Prevention of Adult Antisocial Behaviour.* Cambridge: Cambridge University Press.

Lösel, F. & Bliesener, T. (1994) Some high-risk adolescents do not develop conduct problems. A study of protective factors. *International Journal of Behavioral Development,* 17, pp.753-777.

Lösel, F. & Bender, D. (2003) 'Protective factors and resilience', in Farrington, D. P. & Coid, J. W. (eds.) *Early Prevention of Adult Antisocial Behaviour.* Cambridge: Cambridge University Press.

Maguin, E., Hawkins, J. D., Catalano, R. F., Hill, K., Abbott, R. & Herrenkohl, T. (1995) *Risk factors measured at three ages for violence at age 17-18.* Paper presented to the American Society of Criminology Conference (November).

Malinosky-Rummell, R. & Hansen D. J. (1993) Long-term consequences of childhood physical abuse. *Psychological Bulletin,* 114, pp.68-79.

Markie-Dadds, C. & Sanders, M. R. (in press) Self-directed Triple P (positive parenting program) for mothers with children at-risk of development conduct problems. *Behavioural and Cognitive Psychotherapy.*

Mason, W. A., Kosterman, R., Hawkins, J. D., Haggerty, K. P. & Spoth, R. L. (2003) Reducing adolescents' growth in substance use and delinquency: Randomized trial effects of a parent-training prevention intervention. *Prevention Science,* 4, pp.203-212.

McAuley, C., Knapp, M., Beecham, J., McCurry, N. & Sleed, M. (2004) *Young families under stress: Outcomes and costs of Home-Start support.* York: Joseph Rowntree Foundation.

McCord, J. (1982) A longitudinal view of the relationship between paternal absence and crime, in Gunn, J. & Farrington, D. P. (eds.) *Abnormal Offenders, delinquency, and the Criminal Justice System*, pp.113-28 Chichester: Wiley.

McGee, R., Sylva, P. A. & Williams, S. (1984) Perinatal, neurological, environmental and developmental characteristics of seven-year old children with stable behaviour problems. *Journal of Child Psychology and Psychiatry*, 25, pp.573-586.

Moffitt, T. E. (1993) Adolescence-Limited and Life-Course Persistent Antisocial Behavior: A Developmental Taxonomy. *Psychological Review*, 100 (4), pp.674-701.

Moore, K. J., Sprengelmeyer, P. G. & Chamberlain, P. (2001) Community-based treatment for adjudicated delinquents: The Oregon Social Learning Center's "Monitor" Multidimensional Treatment Foster Care Program *Residential Treatment for Children and Youth* 18, pp.87-97.

Moran P., Ghate D. & van der Merwe, A. (2004) (2004) *What Works in Parenting Support? A review of the international evidence*. Nottingham: DfES.

Mrazek, P. J. & Haggerty R. J. (eds.) (1994) *Reducing Risks for Mental Disorders: Frontiers for Preventive Intervention Research*. Washington DC: Institute of Medicine / National Academy Press.

Nagin, D. S., Farrington, D. P. & Moffitt, T. E. (1995) Life-course trajectories of different types of offenders, *Criminology*, 33, pp.111-139.

Offord, D. R., Boyle, M. H., Racine, Y. A., Fleming, J. E., Cadman, D. T., Blum, H. M., Byrne, C., Links, P. S., Lipman, E. L. & Macmillan, H. L. (1992) Outcome, prognosis and risk in a longitudinal follow-up study. *Journal of the American Academy of Child and Adolescent Psychiatry*, 31 (5), pp.916-923.

Ogden, T. & Halliday-Boykins, C. A. (2004) Multisystemic treatment of antisocial adolescents in Norway: Replication of clinical outcomes outside of the US. *Child and Adolescent Mental Health*, 9 (2), pp.77-83.

Ogden, T., & Hagen , K. A. (2006) Multisystemic therapy of serious behavior problems in youth: Sustainability of therapy effectiveness two years after intake. *Child and Adolescent Mental Health*, 11 (3), pp.142-149.

Olds, D. (1998) *Blueprints for Violence Prevention: Nurse-Family Partnership*. Colorado, U.S.: Center for the Study and Prevention of Violence.

Olds, D. L., Henderson, C. R., Chamberlain, R. and Tatelbaum, R. (1986) Improving the delivery of prenatal care and outcomes of pregnancy: A randomized trial of nurse home visitation. *Pediatrics*, 77 (1), pp.16-28.

Olds, D. L., Henderson, C. R., Phelps, C. Kitzman, H. & Hanks, C. (1993) Effect of prenatal and infancy nurse home visitation on government spending. *Med Care*, 31 (2), pp.155-74.

Olds, D. L., Eckenrode, J., Henderson, C. R., Kitzman, H., Powers, J., Cole, R., Sidora, K., Morris, P. Pettitt, L. M. & Luckey, D. (1997) Long-term effects of home visitation on maternal life course and child abuse and neglect: Fifteen-year follow-up of a randomized trial. *The Journal of the American Medical Association*, 278, pp.637-643.

Olds, D. L., Henderson, C. R.,(Jnr), Cole, R., Eckenrode, J., Kitzman, H., Luckey, D., Pettitt, L., Sidora, K., Morris, P. & Powers, J. (1998) Long-term effects of nurse home visitation on children's criminal & antisocial behaviour. *Journal of the American Medical Association*, 280, pp.1238-1244.

Olds, D., Hill, P. & Rumsey, E. (1998) Prenatal and Early Childhood Nurse Home Visitation. *Juvenile Justice Bulletin*.

Olds, D. L., Robinson, J., O'Brien, R., Luckey, D., Pettitt, L. M., Henderson, C. R., Ng, R. K., Sheff, K. L., Korfmacher, J., Hiatt, S. and Talmi, A. (2002) Home visiting by paraprofessionals and by nurses: A randomized, controlled trial. *Pediatrics*, 110 (3), pp.486-496.

Olds, D. L., Hill, P. L., O'Brien, R., Racine, D. & Moritz, P. (2003) Taking preventative intervention to scale: The Nurse-Family Partnership. *Cognitive and Behavioral Practice*, 10, pp.278-290.

Olds, D. L., Kitzman, H., Cole, R., Robinson, J., Sidora, K., Luckey, D., Henderson, C. R., Hanks, C., Bondy, J. & Holmberg, J. (2004a) Effects of nurse home-visiting on maternal life course and child development: Age 6 follow up results of a randomized trial. *Pediatrics*, 114 (6), pp.1550-1559.

Olds, D. L., Robinson, J., Pettitt, L., Luckey, D. W., Holmberg, J., Ng, R. K., Isacks, K., Sheff, K. & Henderson, C. R. (2004b) Effects of home visits by paraprofessionals and by nurses: Age 4 follow-up results of a randomized trial. *Pediatrics*, 114 (6), pp.1560-1568.

Olweus, D. (1979) Stability of Aggressive Reaction Patterns in Males: a review. *Psychological Bulletin*, 86, pp.852-875.

Olweus, D. (1991) 'Bully/Victim Problems among Schoolchildren: basic facts and effects of a school-based intervention program', in Pepler, D.J. & Rubin, K. (eds.) *The Development and Treatment of Childhood Aggression*. Hillside, New Jersey: Erlbaum.

O'Neill, H. & Woodward. R. (2002) Evaluation of the Parenting Wisely CD-ROM Parent-Training Programme: An Irish Replication. *Irish Journal of Psychology*, 23(1-2), pp.62-72. http://www.familyworksinc.com/research_articles/O_Neillms.doc accessed 29.6.06

Patterson, G. R. (1982) *Coercive Family Process*. Oregon: Castalia.

Patterson, G. R. & Narrett, C. M. (1990) The development of a reliable and valid treatment program for aggressive young children. *International Journal of Mental Health*, 19 (3) pp.19-26.

Patterson, G. R., & Yoerger, K. (1997) 'A developmental model for late-onset delinquency', in Osgood, D. W. (ed.) *Motivation and delinquency: Nebraska Symposium on Motivation* (Vol. 44, pp.119-177). Lincoln, Nebraska: University of Nebraska Press.

Patterson, G. R., Forgatch, M. S., Yoerger, K. L. & Stoolmiller, M. (1998) Variables that initiate and maintain an early-onset trajectory for juvenile offending. *Development and Psychopathology*, 10, pp.531-547.

Patterson, J., Barlow, J., Mockford, C., Klimes, I., Pyper, C. & Stewart-Brown, S. (2002) Improving Mental Health Through Parenting Programmes: Block Randomised Controlled Trial. *Archives of Disease in Childhood*, Vol. 87, pp.472-477.

Pawlby, S. J., Mills, A. & Quinton, D. (1997a) Vulnerable adolescent girls: Opposite sex relationships. *Journal of Child Psychology and Psychiatry*, 38, pp.909-920.

Pawlby, S J., Mills, A., Taylor, A. & Quinton, D (1997b) Adolescent friendships mediating childhood adversity and adult outcome. *Journal of Adolescence*, 20, pp.633-644.

Potter, D. & Mulkern, V. (2004) *Therapeutic Foster Care: Issue Brief.* US: Rutgers Center for State Health Policy.

Purdie, N., Hattie, J. & Carroll, A. (2002) A review of research on interventions for attention deficit hyperactivity disorder; what works best? *Review of Educational Research*, Vol. 72, pp.61-99.

Quinton, D. & Rutter, M. (1988) *Parenting breakdown: the making and breaking of inter-generational links.* Aldershot: Avebury.

Radke-Yarrow, M., and Sherman, T. (1990) Hard growing: Children who Survive, in Rolf, J., Masten, A. S., Cicchetti, D., Nuechterlein, K. H. & Weintraub, S. (Eds.), *Risk and protective factors in the development of psychopathology* (pp.97-119). New York: Cambridge University Press.

Reddy, L. A. & Pfeiffer, S. (1997) Effectiveness of Treatment Foster Care with children and adolescents: A review of outcome studies. *Journal of the American Academy of Child and Adolescent Psychiatry*, 36 (5), pp.581-588.

Reid, M. J., Webster-Stratton, C. & Beauchaine, T. P. (2001) Parent training in Head Start: A comparison of program response among African American, Asian American, Caucasian, and Hispanic mothers. *Prevention Science*, 2 (4) pp.209-227.

Robins, L. N. (1966) *Deviant Children Grown Up: a Sociological and Psychiatric Study of Sociopathic Personality.* Huntington, NY: Krieger.

Robins, L. N. (1978) Sturdy childhood predictors of adult antisocial behaviour: replications from longitudinal studies. *Psychological Medicine*, 8, pp.611-622.

Robins, L. N., Tipp, J. & Przybeck T. R. (1991) 'Antisocial personality', in Robins, L. N. & Regier, D. A. (eds.) *Psychiatric Disorders in America.* New York: Free Press.

Rutter, M. (1978) 'Family, area and school influences in the genesis of conduct disorder', in Hersov, L., Berger, M. & Shaffer, D. (eds.) *Aggression and Antisocial Behaviour in Childhood and Adolescence.* Oxford: Pergamon Press.

Rutter, M. (1979) Protective factors in children's responses to stress and disadvantage. In M.W. Kent and J.E. Rolf (Eds.) *Primary Prevention of Psychopathology, vol. 3: Social Competence in Children*, pp.49-74. Hanover, NH: University Press of New England.

Rutter, M (1985) Resilience in the face of adversity: Protective factors and resistance to psychiatric disorder. *British Journal of Psychiatry*, 147, pp.598-691.

Rutter, M. (1990) 'Psychosocial Resilience and Protective Mechanisms', in Rolf, J., Masten, A. S., Cicchetti, D., Neuchterlein, K. H. & Weintraub, S. (eds.) *Risk and Protective Factors in the Development of Psychopathology*. Cambridge: Cambridge University Press.

Rutter, M. (1996) Transitions and turning points in developmental psychopathology: As applied to the age span between childhood and mid-adulthood. *International Journal of Behavioral Development*, 19, pp.603-626.

Rutter, M. & Garmezy, N. (1983) Developmental psychopathology, in Hetherington, E.M. (ed.). *Socialization, personality, and child development, vol 4: Mussen's Handbook of Child Psychology*, 4th ed, pp.775-911. New York: Wiley.

Rutter, M., Giller, H. & Hagell, A. (1998) *Antisocial Behavior by Young People*. Cambridge: Cambridge University Press.

Sanders, M. R. (1999) Triple P-Positive Parenting Program: Towards an empirically validated multilevel parenting and family support strategy for the prevention of behaviour and emotional problems in children *Clinical Child and Family Psychology Review*, 2(2),pp.71-90.

Sanders, M. R., Cleghorn, D., Shepherd, R. W. & Patrick, M. (1996) Predictors of clinical improvement in children with recurrent abdominal pain. *Behavioural and Cognitive Psychotherapy*, 24, pp.27-38

Sanders, M. R. & Glynn, T. (1981) Training parents in behavioural self-management: an analysis of generalization and maintenance. *Journal of Applied Behaviour Analysis*, 14 (3), pp.223-237.

Sanders, M. R., Markie-Dadds, C., Tully, L. A. & Bor, W. (2000) The Triple P-Positive Parenting Program: A comparison of enhanced, standard and self-directed behavioral family intervention for parents of children with early onset conduct problems. *Journal of Consulting and Clinical Psychology*, 68, pp.624-640.

Sanders, M. R., Markie-Dadds, C. & Turner, K. M. (2003) *Theoretical, Scientific and Clinical Foundations of the Triple-P Positive Parenting Program: A Population Approach to the Promotion of Parenting Competence*. Parenting Practice and Research Monograph No 1. Parenting and Family Support Centre, University of Queensland.

Sanders, M. R. & McFarland, M. (2000) Treatment of depressed mothers with disruptive children: A controlled evaluation of cognitive behavioural family intervention. *Behavior Therapy*, 31 pp.89-112.

Santos, A. B., Henggeler, S. W., Burns, B. J., Arana, G. W. & Meisler, N. (1995) Research on field-based services: Models for reform in the delivery of mental health care to population with complex clinical problems. *American Journal of Psychiatry*, 152 (8), pp.1111-1123.

Schaeffer, C. M., & Borduin, C. M. (2005) Long-term follow-up to a randomized clinical trial of multisystemic therapy with serious and violent juvenile offenders. *Journal of Consulting and Clinical Psychology*, 73 (3), pp.445-453.

Schoenwald, S. K., Ward, D. M., Henggeler, S. W., Pickrel, S. G. & Patel, H. (1996) Multisystemic therapy treatment of substance abusing or dependent adolescent offenders: Costs of reducing incarceration, inpatient, and residential placement. *Journal of Child and Family Studies*, 5 (4), pp.431-444.

Schweinhart, L. J., Montie, J., Xiang, Z., Barnett, W. S., Belfield, C. R., & Nores, M. (2005) *Lifetime effects: The High/Scope Perry Preschool study through age 40.* Monographs of the High/Scope Educational Research Foundation, 14. Ypsilanti, MI: High/Scope Press.

Scott, S., Knapp, M., Henderson, J. & Maughan, B. (2001) Financial cost of social exclusion: follow up study of antisocial children into adulthood. *British Medical Journal*, 323 (7306) p.191.

Scott, S., Spender, Q., Doolan, M., Jacobs, B. & Aspland, H. C. (2001) Multicentre controlled trial of parenting groups for childhood antisocial behavior in clinical practice. *British Medical Journal*, 323 (7306) p.194.

Scott, S. and Sylva, K. (2003) *The 'SPOKES' projects: a preventive trial to improve disadvantaged children's life chances by boosting their social functioning and reading skills.* London: Department of Health .

Scott, S., O'Connor, T. & Futh, A. (2006) *What makes parenting programmes work in disadvantaged areas? The PALS trial .* York: Joseph Rowntree Foundation.

Sexton, T. L. & Alexander, J. F. (1999) *Functional Family Therapy: Principles of Clinical Assessment and Implementation.* Henderson, N.V.: RCH Enterprises.

Sexton, T. L. & Alexander, J. F. (2000) Functional Family Therapy. *Juvenile Justice Bulletin,* December 2000.

Sherman, L. W., Gottfredson, D. C., MacKenzie, D., Eck, J., Reuter, P. & Bushway, S. (1997) *Preventing crime: What works, what doesn't, what's promising: A report to the U.S. Congress.* University of Maryland.

Shure, M. B. & Spivack, G. (1982) Interpersonal problem solving in young children: A cognitive approach to prevention. *American Journal of Community Psychology,* 10, pp.341-356.

Spoth, R., Redmond, C. & Shin, C. (2000) Reducing adolescents' aggressive and hostile behaviours: Randomized trial effects of a brief family intervention four years past baseline. *Archives of Pediatrics and Adolescent Medicine,* 154, pp.1248-1257

Stone, W. L., Bendell, R. D. & Field, T. M. (1988) The impact of socioeconomic status on teenage mothers and children who receive early intervention. *Journal of Applied Developmental Psychology*, 9, pp.391-408.

Sutton, C., Utting, D. & Farrington, D. (2004) *Support from the Start*. Nottingham: DfES.

Swanson, J. M. et al (2002) Response to the commentary on the Multidimensional Treatment Study of ADHD (MTA): Mining the meaning of MTA. *Journal of Abnormal Child Psychology*, 30, pp.327-332.

Timmons-Mitchell, J., Bender, M. B., Kishna, M. A., & Mitchell, C. C. (2006) An independent effectiveness trial of multisystemic therapy with juvenile justice youth. *Journal of Clinical Child and Adolescent Psychology*, 35 (2), pp.227-236.

Tremblay, R. E., Vitaro, F., Bertrand, L., LeBlanc, M., Beauchesne, H., Boileau, H. & David, L. (1992) 'Parent and child training to prevent early onset of delinquency: The Montreal longitudinal Experimental Study', in McCord, J. & Tremblay, R. (eds.), *Preventing Antisocial Behavior: Interventions from Birth through Adolescence*. New York: The Guilford Press.

Tremblay, R. E., Pagani-Kurtz, L., Vitaro, F., Mâsse, L.C., & Pihl, R. O. (1995) A bimodal preventive intervention for disruptive kindergarten boys: Its impact through mid-adolescence. *Journal of Consulting and Clinical Psychology*, 63, pp.560-568.

Turner, K. M., Sanders, M. R. & Wall, C. R. (1994) Behavioural parent training versus dietary education in the treatment of children with persistent feeding difficulties. *Behaviour Change*, 11 (4), pp.242-258.

Utting, D., Bright, J. & Henricson, C. (1993) *Crime and the family: Improving child-rearing and preventing delinquency*. London: Family Policy Studies Centre.

Webster-Stratton, C. (1984) Randomized Trial of Two Parent Training Programs for Families with Conduct-Disordered Children. *Journal of Consulting and Clinical Psychology*, Vol. 52 (4), pp.666-678.

Webster-Stratton, C. (1990) Long-term follow-up of families with young conduct-problem children: From preschool to grade school. *Journal of Clinical Child Psychology*, 19, pp.144-149.

Webster-Stratton, C. (1998a) 'Parent-training with low-income families', in Lutzker, J. R. (ed.) *Handbook of Child Abuse Research and Treatment*. New York: Plenum Press.

Webster-Stratton, C. (1998b) Preventing conduct problems in Head Start children: Strengthening parent competencies. *Journal of Consulting and Clinical Psychology*. Vol. 66, pp.715-730.

Webster-Stratton, C. (2001) *Blueprints for Violence Prevention: The Incredible Years, parents, teacher and child training series*. Colorado, U.S.: Institute of Behavioral Science, University of Colorado.

Webster-Stratton, C. & Hammond, M. (1997) Treating children with early on-set conduct problems: A comparison of child and parent training interventions. *Journal of Consulting and Clinical Psychology*, 65 (1), pp.93-109.

Werner, E. E., & Smith, R. S., (1982) *Vulnerable but invincible: A longitudinal study of resilient children and youth*. New York: McGraw-Hill.

West, D. J. (1982) *Delinquency: its roots, careers and prospects*. London: Heineman

Widom, C. S. (1989) The cycle of violence. *Science*, 244, pp.160-166.

Widom, C. S. & Ames, M. A. (1994) Criminal consequences of childhood sexual victimization. *Child Abuse and Neglect*, 18, pp.303-318.

Yoshikawa, H. (1994) Prevention as cumulative protection: Effects of early family support and education on chronic delinquency and its risks. *Psychological Bulletin*, 115, pp.28-54

Zoccolillo, M., Pickles, A., Quinton, D. & Rutter, M. (1992) The outcome of childhood conduct disorder: Implications for defining adult personality disorder and conduct disorder. *Psychological Medicine*, 22 pp.971-86.